10.99

heart

Collection

First published by Faber Music Ltd in 2010
Bloomsbury House 74–77 Great Russell Street London WC1B 3DA

Arranged by Olly Weeks & Alex Davis
Edited by Lucy Holliday

Printed in England by Caligraving Ltd

The text paper used in this publication is a virgin fibre product that is manufactured in the EU.The wood fibre used is only sourced from managed forests using sustainable forestry principles.
This paper is 100% recyclable

ISBN10: 0-571-53460-0
EAN13: 978-0-571-53460-9

To buy Faber Music publications or to find out about the full range of titles available, please contact your local music retailer or Faber Music sales enquiries:

Faber Music Ltd, Burnt Mill, Elizabeth Way, Harlow,
CM20 2HX England
Tel: +44(0)1279 82 89 82
Fax: +44(0)1279 82 89 83
sales@fabermusic.com fabermusic.com

BAD DAY

Words and Music by Daniel Powter

Fm7 B♭ E♭ A♭add9
and I don't need you to car - ry on. You're stand-ing in line just to hit a new low,
mf
B♭ E♭ A♭add9 B♭
you're fak-ing a smile with a cof-fee to go.
Cm E♭/B♭ A♭ E♭/G
Tell me your life's been way off line, you're fall-ing to pie - ces ev - 'ry time
Fm7 B♭ N.C.
and I don't need you to car - ry on. 'Cos you had a bad

E♭ A♭ Fm7 B♭
19
day, you're tak - ing one down, you sing a sad song just to turn it a - round, you say you don't
f
E♭ A♭ Fm7 B♭
21
know, you tell me don't lie, you work on a smile and you go for a ride. You had a bad
Cm Gm/B♭ A♭ E♭/G
23
day the cam - era don't lie, you're com - ing back down and you real - ly don't mind, you had a bad
Fm7 B♭ E♭ E♭/A♭ B♭7sus4 B♭ A♭
25
day, you had a bad day.
mf

E♭
A♭
B♭7sus4
B♭
Cm
Gm/B♭
28
Well you need a blue sky ho - li - day
A♭
E♭/G
Fm7
31
the point is they laugh at what you say,
and I don't need you to car - ry
B♭
E♭
A♭
33
on.
You had a bad day,
you're tak - ing one down,
you sing a sad
Fm7
B♭
E♭
A♭
35
song just to turn it a - round,
you say you don't know,
you tell me don't lie,
you work on a

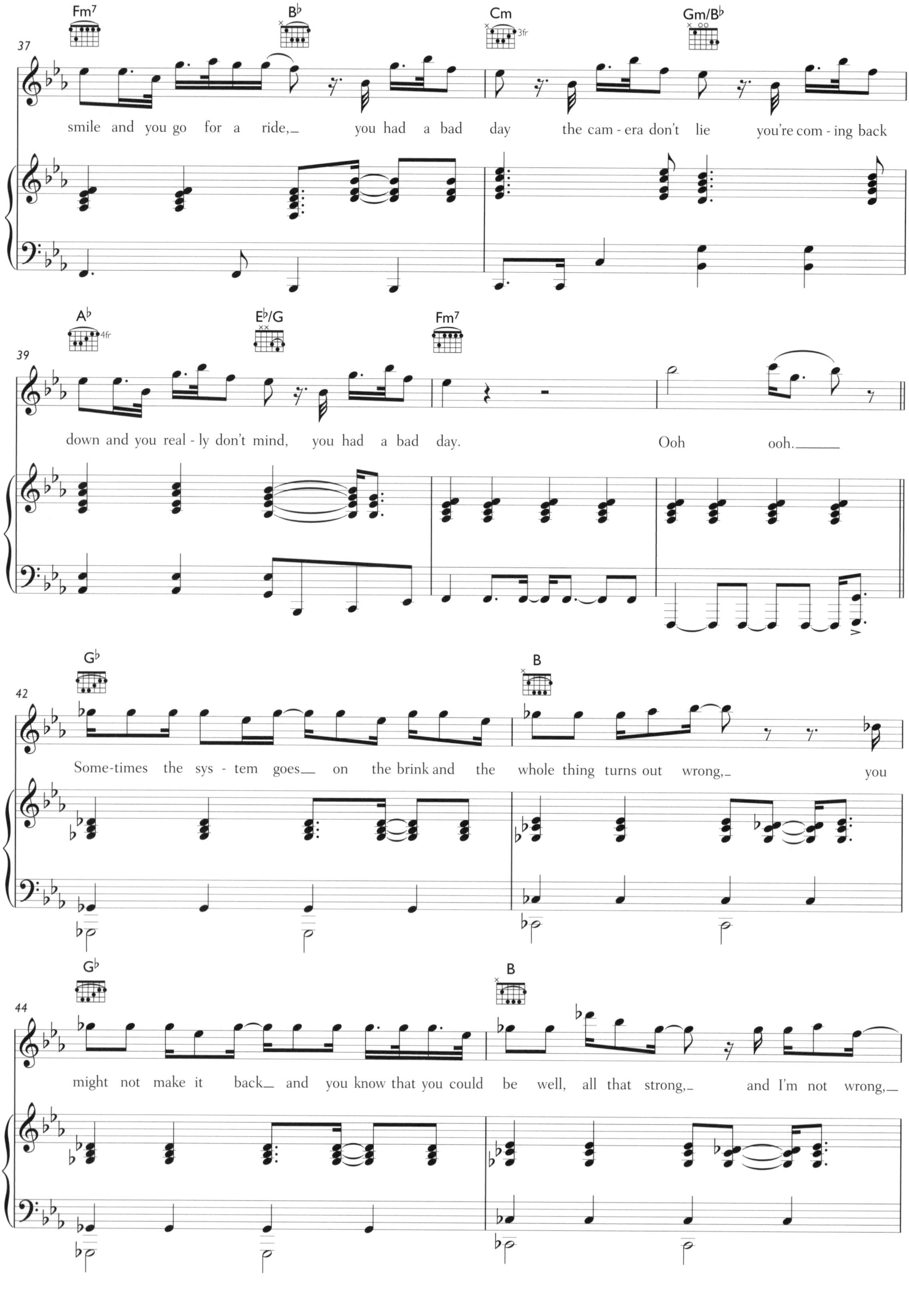
Fm7
B♭
Cm
3fr
Gm/B♭
37
smile and you go for a ride, you had a bad day the cam - era don't lie you're com - ing back
A♭
4fr
E♭/G
Fm7
39
down and you real - ly don't mind, you had a bad day. Ooh ooh.
G♭
B
42
Some-times the sys - tem goes on the brink and the whole thing turns out wrong, you
G♭
B
44
might not make it back and you know that you could be well, all that strong, and I'm not wrong,

E♭/B♭
B♭
46
yeah.
E♭
E♭/A♭
E♭/B♭
48
So where is the pas - sion when need - ed the most?
Oh you and I,
p
E♭
A♭
4fr
B♭
50
you kick up the leaves and the ma - gic is lost,
'cos you had a bad
mp
E♭
A♭
4fr
Fm7
B♭
52
day, you're tak - ing one down, you sing a sad song just to turn it a - round, you say you don't
f

E♭ A♭ Fm7 B♭
54
know, you tell me don't lie, you work on a smile and you go for a ride, you had a bad
Cm Cm/B E♭/B♭ F/A F7/A
56
day, you've seen what you like and how does it feel? One more time, you had a bad day,
A♭ A♭/B♭ F7/A E♭ A♭maj7 Fm7 B♭
58
you had a bad day. Hey had a bad
E♭ A♭maj7 Fm7 B♭
61
repeat to fade
day, hey had a bad

BECAUSE OF YOU

Words and Music by Ben Moody, Kelly Clarkson and David Hodges

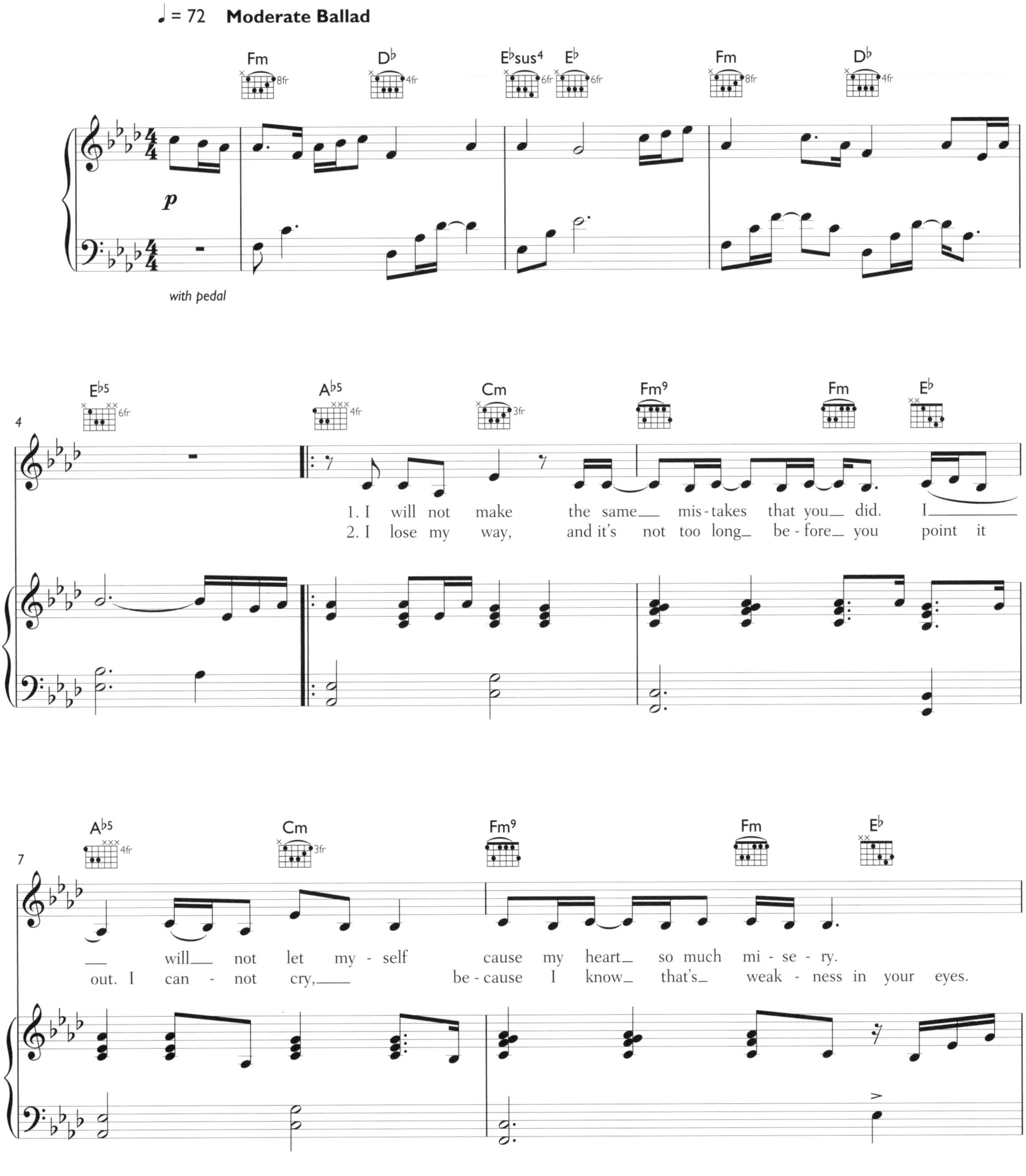
♩ = 72 Moderate Ballad
Fm
D♭
E♭sus4
E♭
Fm
D♭
p
with pedal
E♭5
A♭5
Cm
Fm9
Fm
E♭
1. I will not make the same mis-takes that you did. I
2. I lose my way, and it's not too long be-fore you point it
A♭5
Cm
Fm9
Fm
E♭
will not let my-self cause my heart so much mi-se-ry.
out. I can-not cry, be-cause I know that's weak-ness in your eyes.

A♭5 Cm Fm9 Fm E♭
I will not break the way you did. You fell so hard.
I'm forced to fake a smile, a laugh, ev - 'ry day of my
A♭5 Cm Fm9 Fm E♭5 E♭sus4 E♭
I've learned the hard way to nev-er let it get that far.
life. My heart can't pos-si-bly break when it wasn't ev-en whole to start with.
Be-cause of
Fm D♭maj7 E♭sus4 E♭ E♭sus4 E♭ Fm D♭maj7
you I nev-er stray too far from the side-walk. Be-cause of you I learned to play on the safe side, so I don't
f
E♭ C7 B♭m7 A♭/C
get hurt. Be - cause of you I find it hard to trust not on - ly me,

E♭
C7
D♭maj7
19
but ev-'ry-one a-round me. Be-cause of you, I am a-fraid.
1.
2.
E♭sus2
E♭
Cm
Fm
21
I watched you die, I heard you cry ev-'ry night in your
E♭
Cm
Fm
24
sleep. I was so young; you should have known bet-ter than to lean
E♭
Cm
Fm
26
on me. You nev-er thought of a-ny-one else; you just saw

E♭sus4 E♭ Cm Fm E♭sus4 E♭
28
your pain, and now I cry in the mid-dle of the night for the same damn thing.
E♭sus4 E♭ E♭sus2 E♭5 Fm D♭ E♭ E♭sus4 E♭
31
Be-cause of you I nev-er stray too far from the side-walk. Be-cause of
ff
p
Fm D♭ E♭5 N.C.
34
you I learned to play on the safe side so I don't get hurt. Be-cause of
ff
Gm E♭maj7 F
36
you, I try my hard-est just to for-get ev-'ry-thing. Be-cause of
f

Gm
E♭maj7
F
D7
38
you, I don't know how to let a - ny - one else in. Be-cause of you,
Cm7
B♭/D
F7
D7
40
I'm a-shamed of my life, be-cause it's emp - ty. Be-cause of you,
E♭maj7
F
Gm
E♭
42
I am a - fraid, be-cause of you,
mp
p
F
Fsus4
F5
Gm
E♭
F
45
be-cause of you.

BLEEDING LOVE

Words and Music by Jesse McCartney and Ryan Tedder

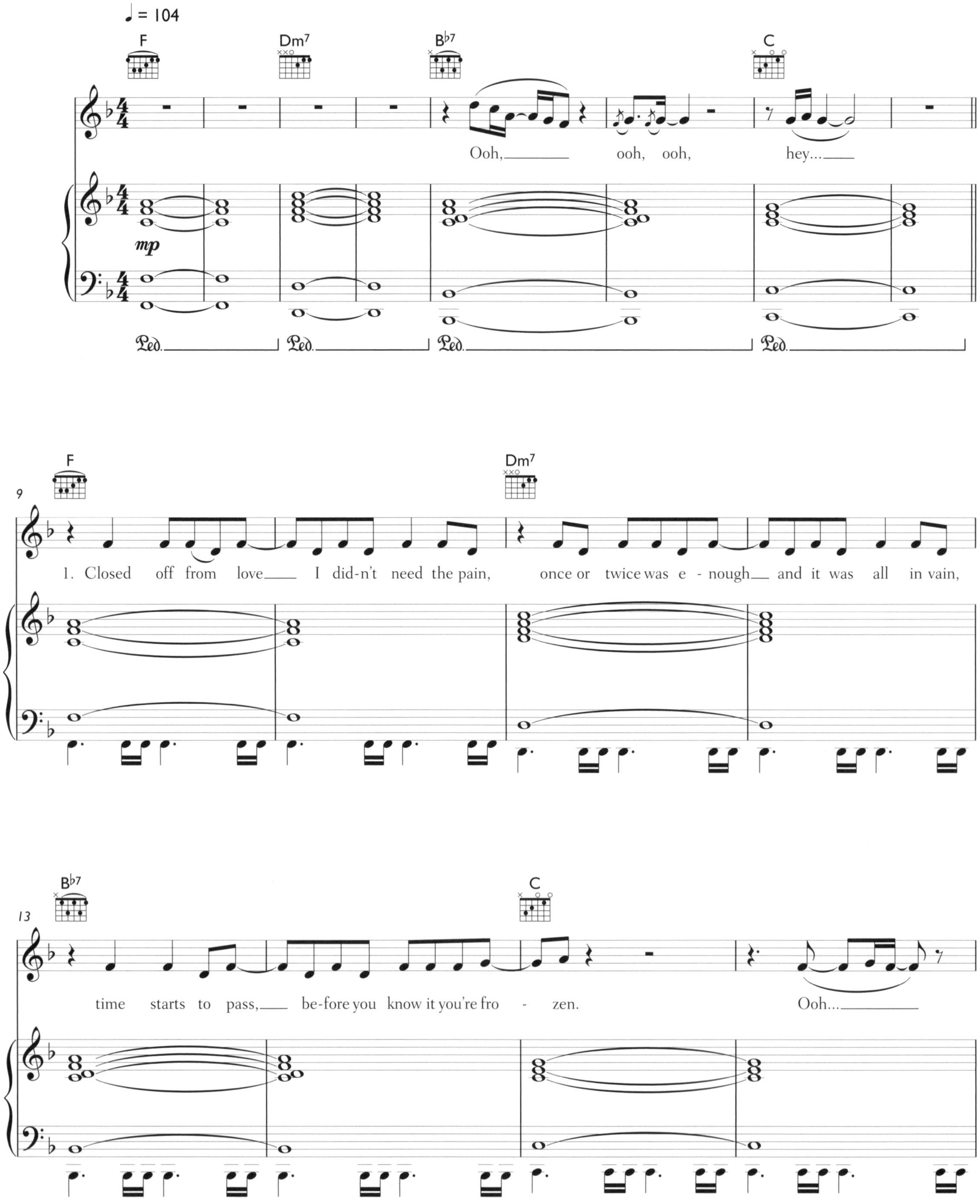
♩ = 104
F
Dm7
B♭7
C
Ooh, ooh, ooh, hey...
mp
Ped.
9
F
Dm7
1. Closed off from love I did-n't need the pain, once or twice was e - nough and it was all in vain,
13
B♭7
C
time starts to pass, be-fore you know it you're fro - zen. Ooh...

F
Dm7
17
But some-thing hap-pened for the ve-ry first time with you, my heart melt-ed to the ground, found some-thing true,
B♭7
C
N.C.
21
and ev-'ry-one's look-ing round, think-ing I'm go-ing cra - zy. Ooh, hey, hey, hey...
F
Dm7
25
But I don't care what they say, I'm in love with you, they try to pull me a-way but they don't know the truth,
mf
B♭7
C
29
my heart's crip-pled by the vein that I keep on clos - ing. You cut me o-pen and I,

F
Dm7
33
keep bleed-ing, keep, keep bleed-ing love, I keep bleed-ing I keep, keep bleed-ing love,
B♭7
C
To Coda
F
37
keep bleed-ing, keep, keep bleed-ing love.
You cut me o-pen...
F
Dm7
43
2. Try-ing hard not to hear but they talk so loud, their pierc-ing sounds fill my ears try to fill me with doubt,
B♭7
Csus4
C
47
yet I know that their goal is to keep me from fall - ing, hey... oh.

F
Dm7
But no-thing's great-er than the risk that comes with your em - brace, and in this world of lone - li-ness I see your face,
Bb7
Csus4
C
D.𝄋 al Coda
N.C.
yet ev-'ry-one a-round me thinks that I'm go-ing cra - zy, may - be, may - be.
Coda
Dm7
Bb
And it's drain - ing all of me, though they find it hard to be - lieve,
F/C
C
I'll be wear-ing these scars for ev - 'ry - one to see.

Dm7
Bb
67
I don't care what they say, I'm in love with you, they try to pull me a-way but they don't know the truth,
p
Ped.
Ped.
C
71
my heart's crip-pled by the vein that I keep on clos - ing, ooh, you cut me o-pen and I
Dm7
Bb7
ad lib. on repeat
75
mf

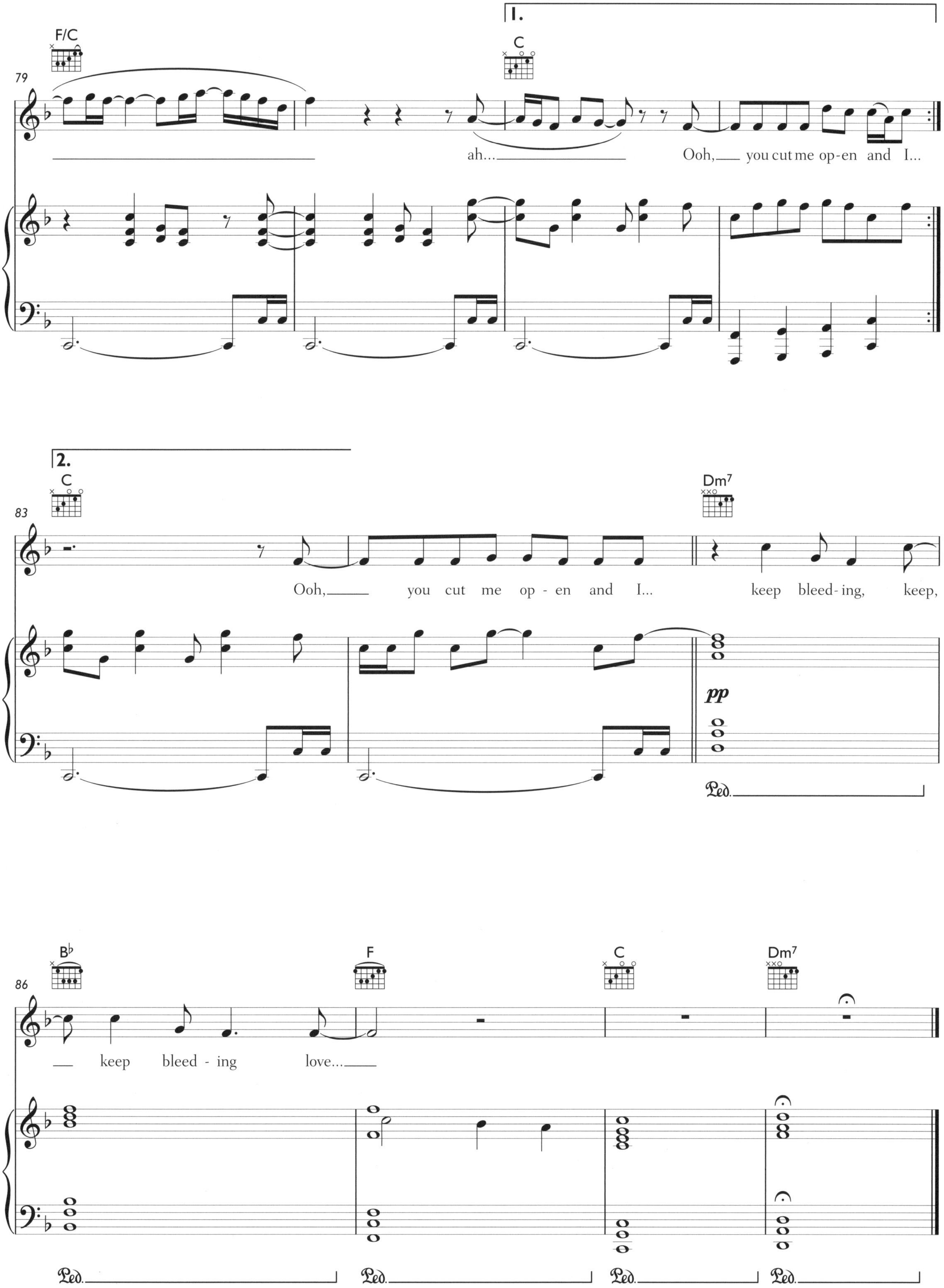
F/C
79
1.
C
ah...
Ooh, you cut me op-en and I...
2.
C
83
Ooh, you cut me op - en and I...
Dm7
keep bleed-ing, keep,
pp
Ped.
B♭
86
F
C
Dm7
keep bleed - ing love...
Ped.
Ped.
Ped.
Ped.

Alexandra Burke

BROKEN HEELS

Words by Savan Kotecha, Nadir Khayat and Bilal Hajji
Music by Savan Kotecha and Nadir Khayat

♩ = 166 **Swing feel**
Original key E♭ minor

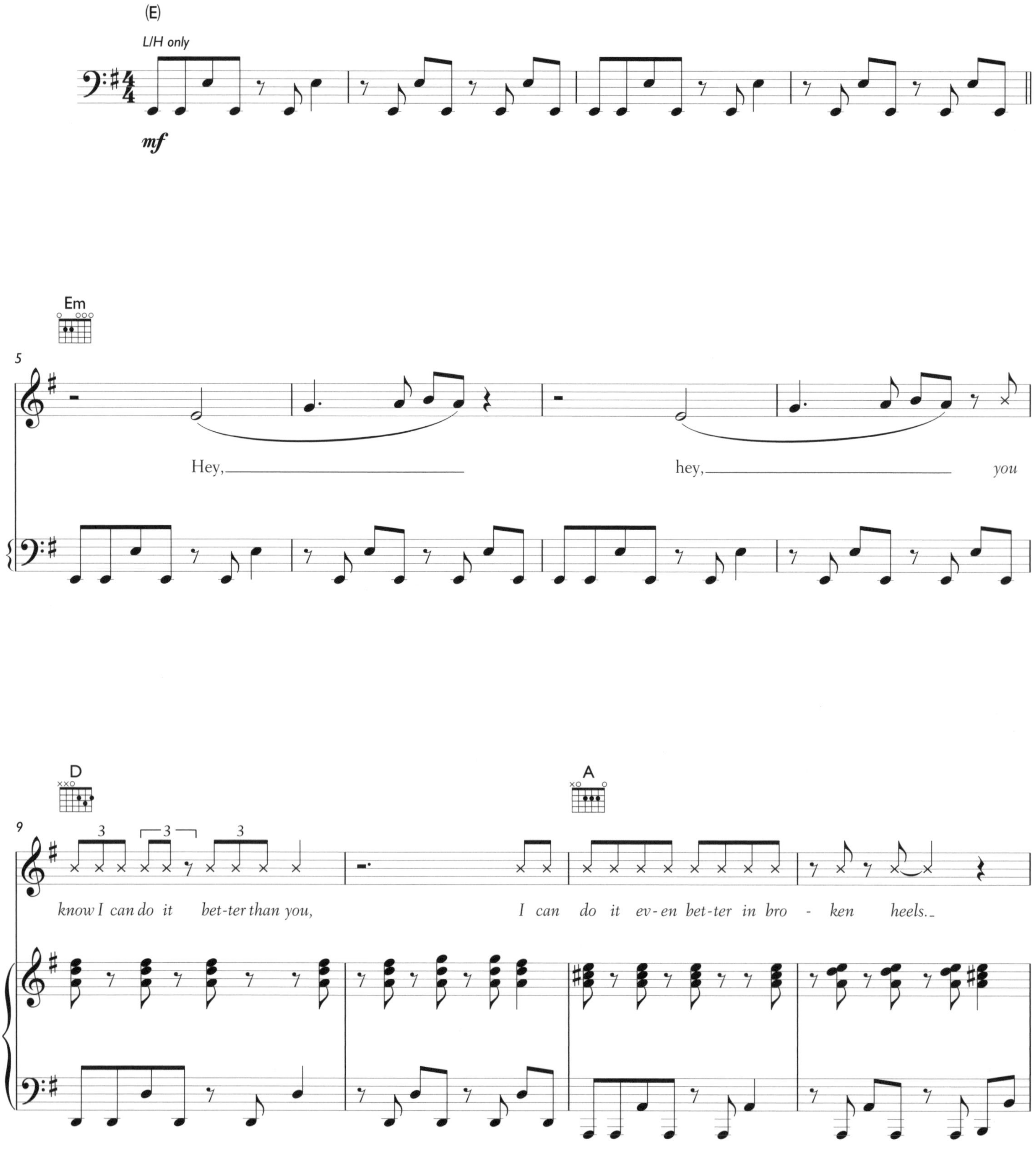

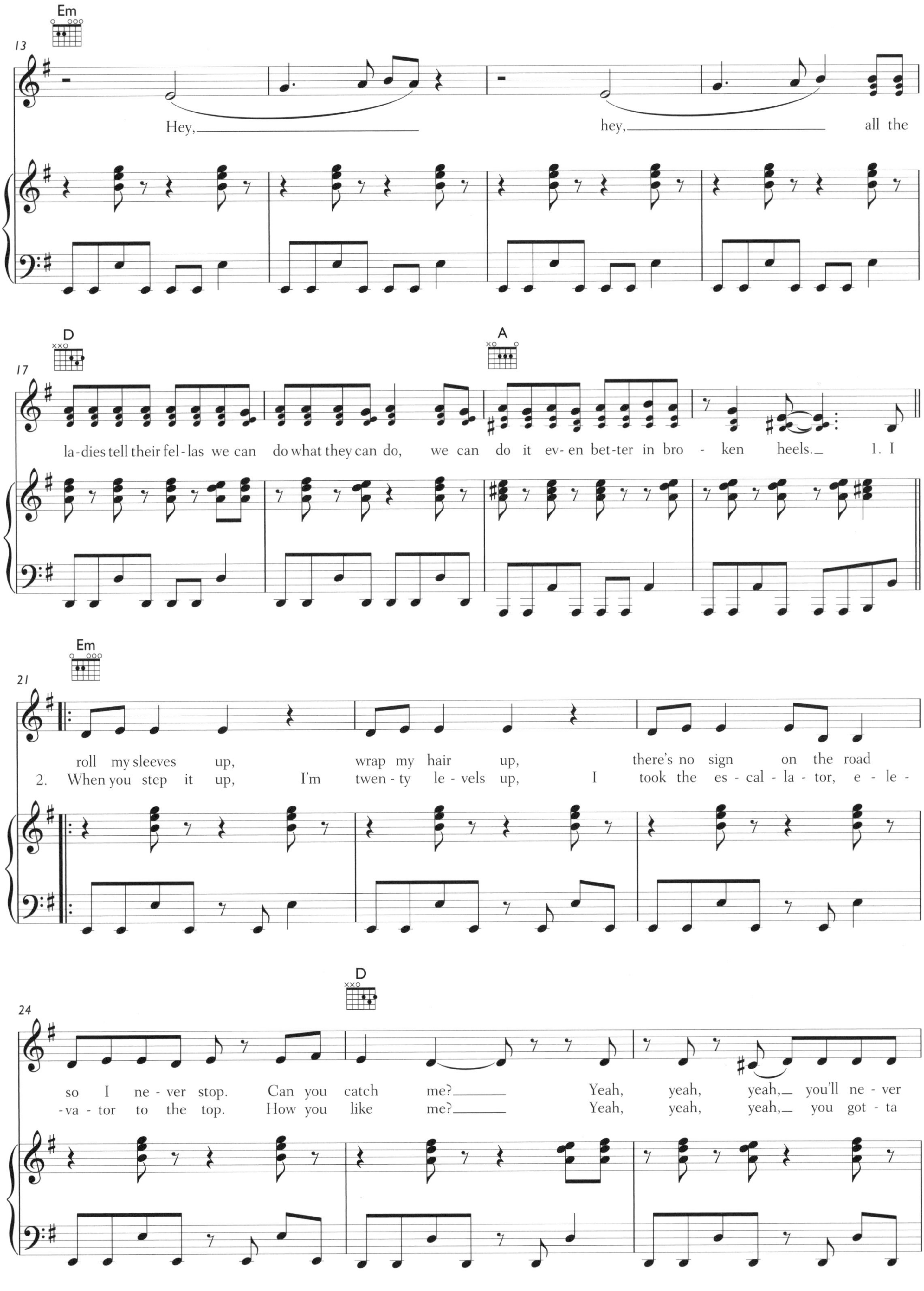
Em
13
Hey, hey, all the
D
A
17
la-dies tell their fel-las we can do what they can do, we can do it ev-en bet-ter in bro - ken heels. 1. I
Em
21
roll my sleeves up, wrap my hair up, there's no sign on the road
2. When you step it up, I'm twen-ty le-vels up, I took the es-cal-la-tor, e-le-
D
24
so I ne-ver stop. Can you catch me? Yeah, yeah, yeah, you'll ne-ver
-va-tor to the top. How you like me? Yeah, yeah, yeah, you got-ta

A
Em
27
catch me. Ay, ay, ay. I'm fresh out the box, (box,)
like me. Ay, ay, ay. Oh you know we rock,
30
fast like a fox, (fox.) Fast - en my shoes, tick tock, twelve-o-clock, you bet-ter
we con-trol the block, what-ev-er's go-ing down, the la-dies take the big-gest cut. We bring the
D
A
33
watch me, yeah, yeah, yeah, sit back and watch me, ay, ay, ay.
par - ty, yeah, yeah, yeah, we bought the par - ty. Ay, ay, ay.
C
D
Em
D
37
You go hard, yes you do, but when I go it's a ma-gic show

C
D
Em
B7
N.C.
41
— oh oh — oh oh, I get it when I want it and I get it — right. —
Em
45
Hey, — hey, — all the
f
D
A
49
la-dies tell their fel-las we can do what they can do, we can do it ev-en bet-ter in bro - ken heels. —
Em
53
Hey, — hey, — all the

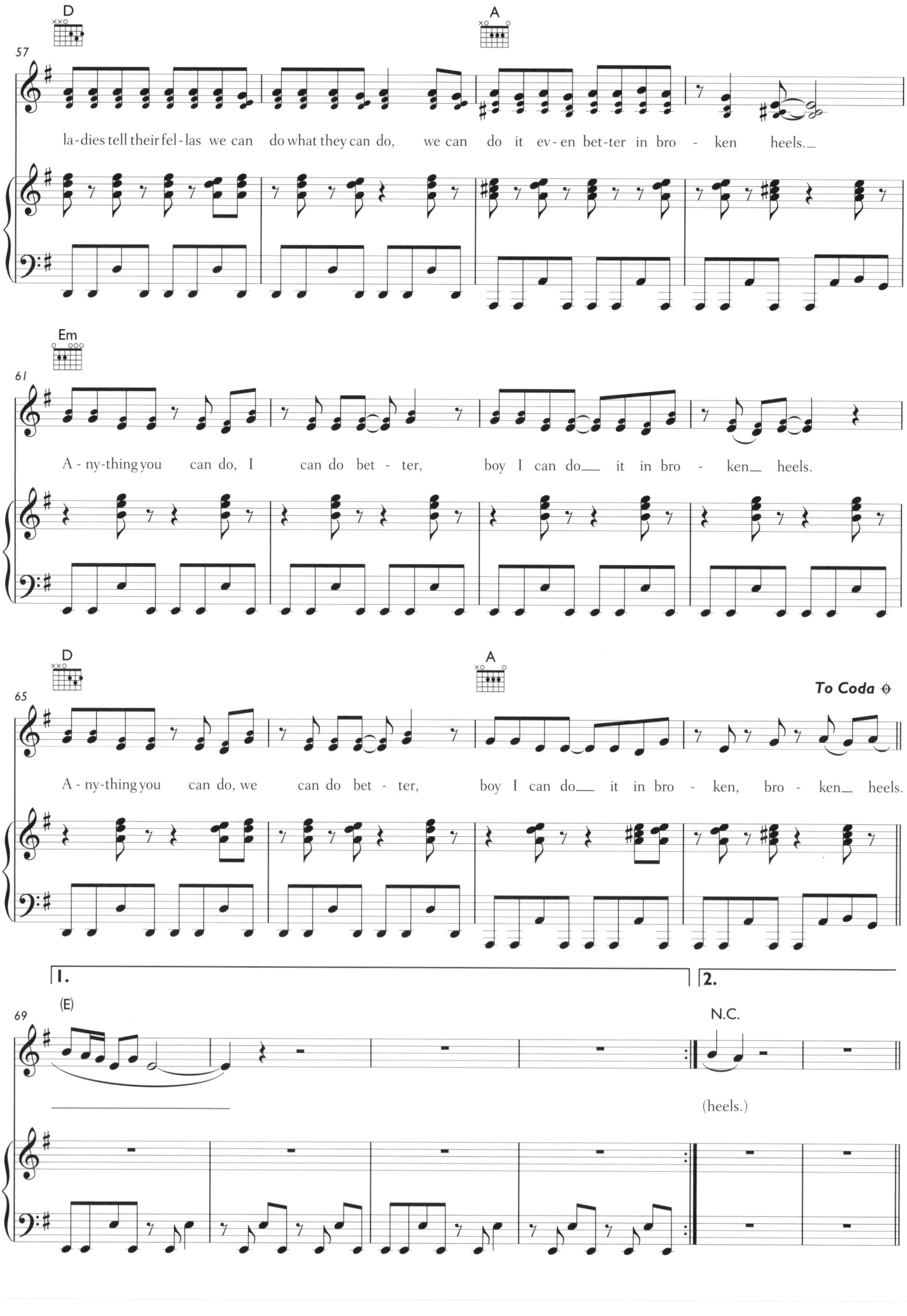
D
A
57
la-dies tell their fel-las we can do what they can do, we can do it ev-en bet-ter in bro - ken heels._
Em
61
A - ny-thing you can do, I can do bet - ter, boy I can do__ it in bro - ken__ heels.
D
A
To Coda
65
A - ny-thing you can do, we can do bet - ter, boy I can do__ it in bro - ken, bro - ken__ heels.
1.
2.
69
(E)
N.C.
(heels.)

Em
C
75
Oh oh oh, oh oh oh oh oh, oh oh oh, oh oh oh oh oh,
mp
1.
2.
D.𝄋 al Coda
G
D
B7♭9/D♯
B7♭9
79
oh oh oh, oh oh oh oh oh, oh oh oh, oh oh oh oh.
oh oh oh.
⊕ Coda
Em
84
A-ny-thing you can do, I can do bet - ter, boy I can do it in bro - ken heels.
D
A
N.C♯.
88
A-ny-thing you can do, we can do bet - ter, boy I can do it in bro - ken, bro - ken heels.

CAN'T FIGHT THE MOONLIGHT

(FROM "COYOTE UGLY")

Words and Music by Diane Warren

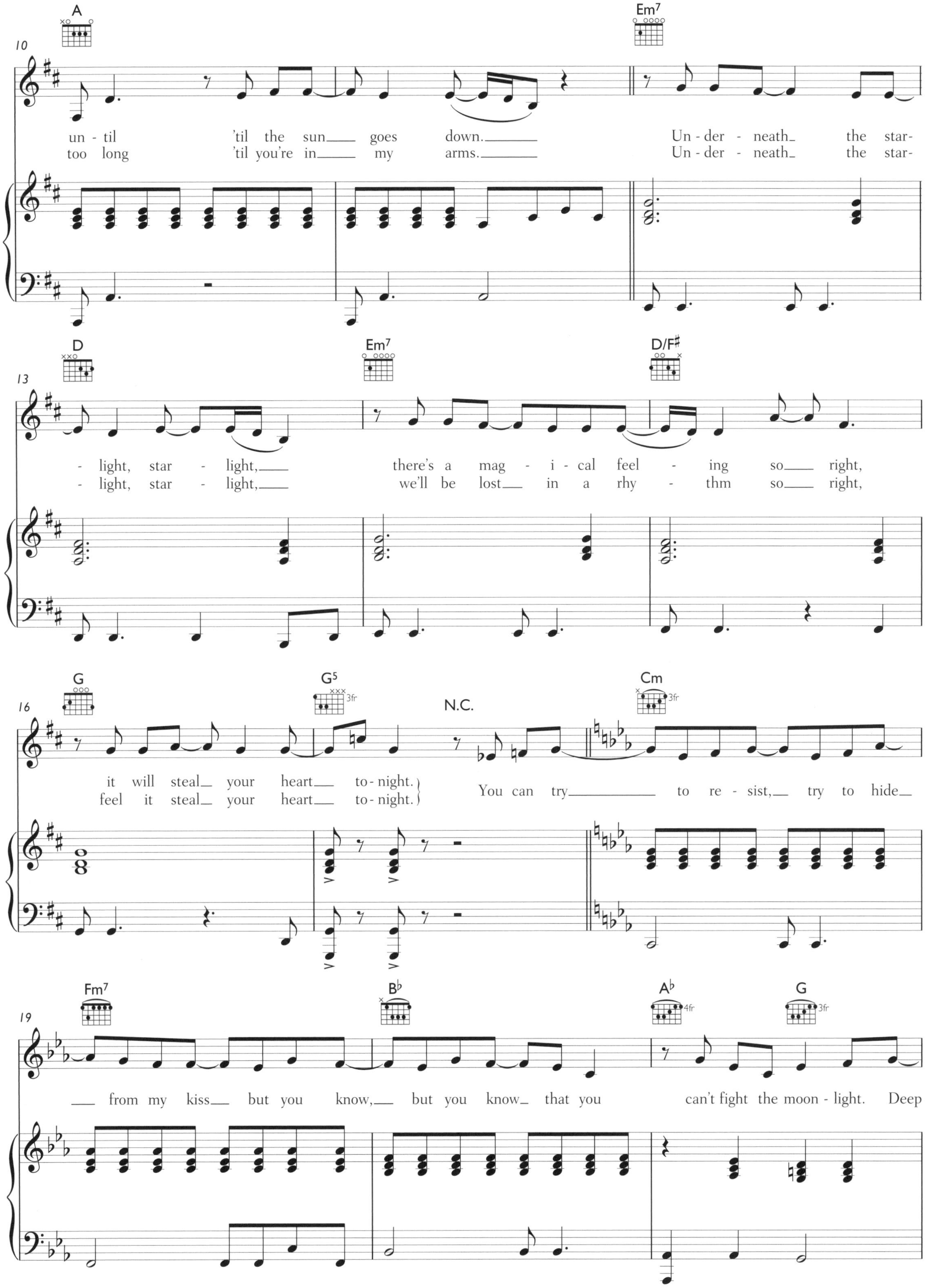

A
Em7
10
un - til 'til the sun goes down. Un - der - neath the star-
too long 'til you're in my arms. Un - der - neath the star-
D
Em7
D/F♯
13
- light, star - light, there's a mag - i - cal feel - ing so right,
- light, star - light, we'll be lost in a rhy - thm so right,
G
G5
3fr
N.C.
Cm
3fr
16
it will steal your heart to - night.
feel it steal your heart to - night.
You can try to re - sist, try to hide
Fm7
B♭
A♭
4fr
G
3fr
19
from my kiss but you know, but you know that you can't fight the moon - light. Deep

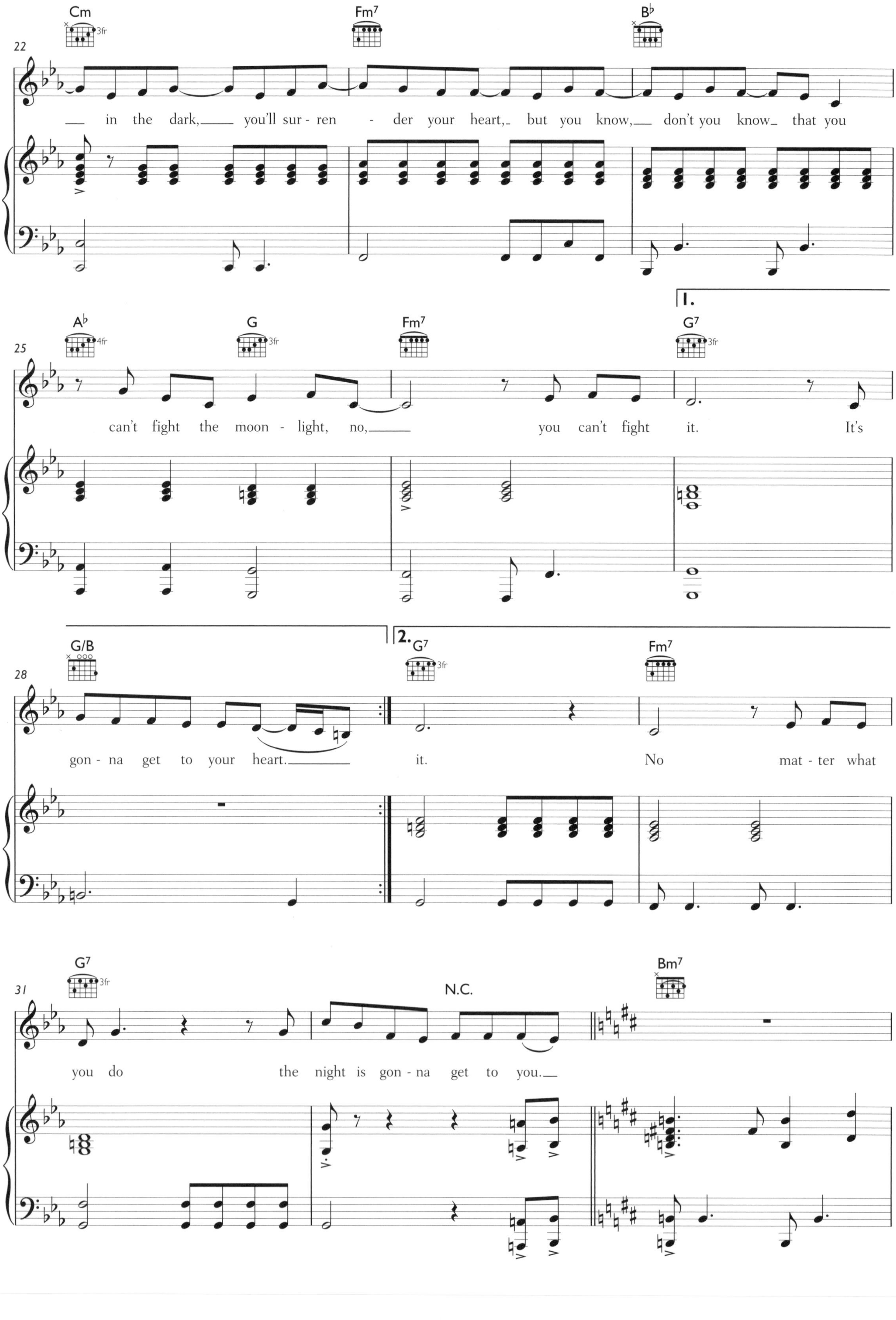
Cm
3fr
Fm7
B♭
22
in the dark, you'll sur - ren - der your heart, but you know, don't you know that you
A♭
4fr
G
3fr
Fm7
1.
G7
3fr
25
can't fight the moon - light, no, you can't fight it. It's
G/B
2.
G7
3fr
Fm7
28
gon - na get to your heart. it. No mat - ter what
G7
3fr
N.C.
Bm7
31
you do the night is gon - na get to you.

Em7
A
34
Can't fight it.
Don't try it, you're ne - ver gon - na win, 'cos,
Fm7
Eb
3fr
Fm7
37
un - der - neath the star - light, star - light,
there's a mag - i - cal feel -
Eb/G
3fr
Ab
4fr
Ab5
4fr
40
- ing so right.
It will steal your heart to - night.
You can try
C#m
4fr
F#m7
B
43
to re - sist, try to hide from my kiss but you know, but you know that you
f
cont. sim.

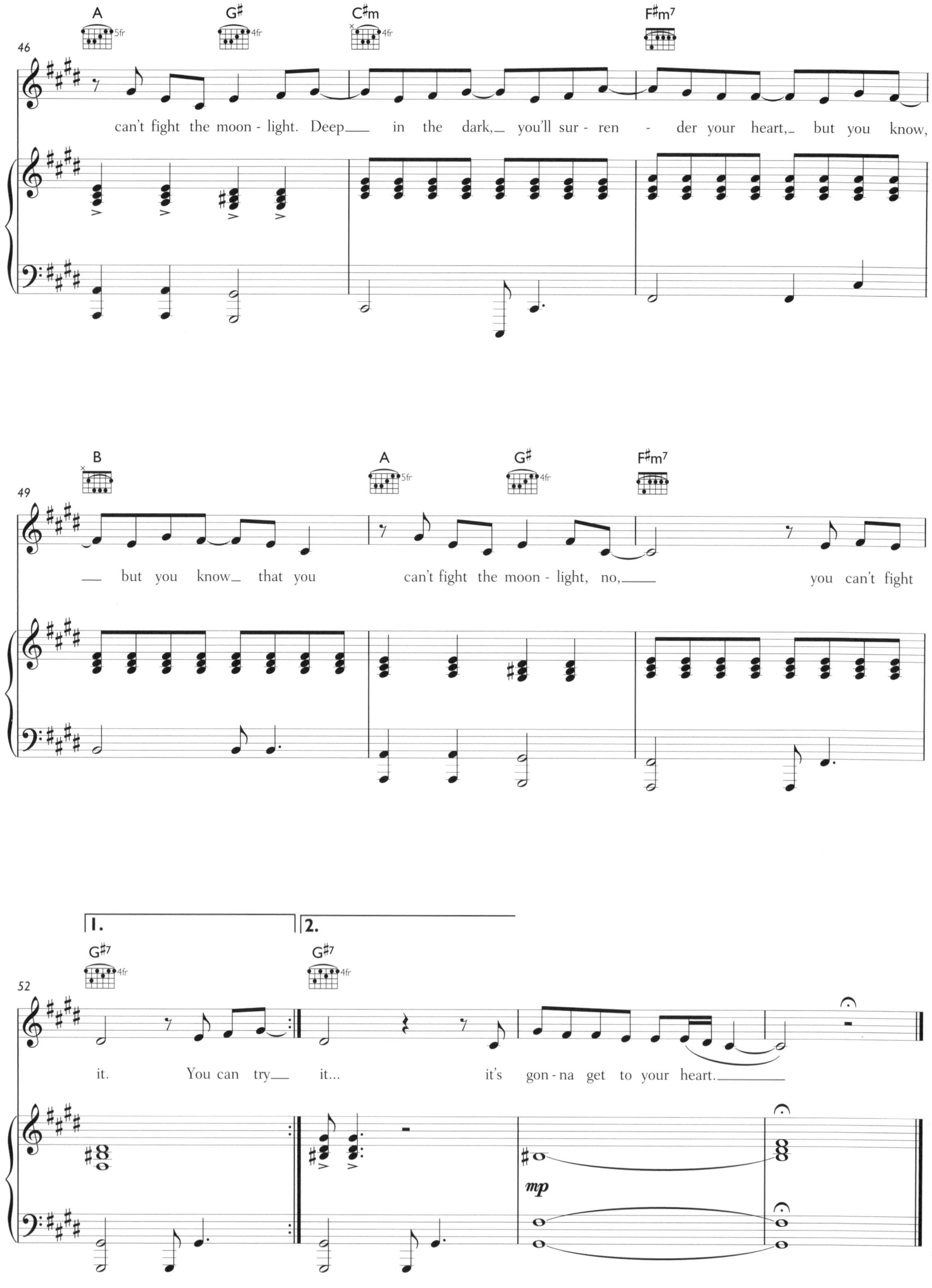
A G# C#m F#m7
5fr 4fr 4fr
46
can't fight the moon - light. Deep in the dark, you'll sur - ren - der your heart, but you know,
B A G# F#m7
5fr 4fr
49
but you know that you can't fight the moon - light, no, you can't fight
1. 2.
G#7 G#7
4fr 4fr
52
it. You can try it... it's gon - na get to your heart.
mp

CLOSER

Words and Music by Mikkel Eriksen, Magnus Beite,
Tor Erik Hermansen, Bernt Stray and Shaffer Smith

Em9
13
like_ she's right there in_ my ear,_ tell - ing me that she wants to own
she's_ the sweet - est taste_ of sin,_ the more I get, the more_ I want,_
Cadd9(♯11) D/C Cadd9(♯11) D/C
17
me,_ to con - trol_ me._
she wants to own_ me._
Come clo -
Em9 D/E Em9 D/E Em D/E
21
- ser,_ come clos - er._
And I just
Cadd9(♯11) D/C Cadd9(♯11) D/C
25
_ can't pull_ my - self_ a - way,_ un-der a_ spell I_ can't break,_ I just_ can't stop,
mf

Em9 D/E Em9
29
I just can't stop, I just can't stop, I just can't stop,
D/E Em D/E Cadd9(♯11) D/C
32
and I just can't bring my - self a - way but I don't
Cadd9(♯11) D/C Em9
35
want to es - cape, I just can't stop, I just can't stop,
D/E Em9 D/E Em D/E
38
To Coda
I just can't stop, I just can't stop, I just can't stop.

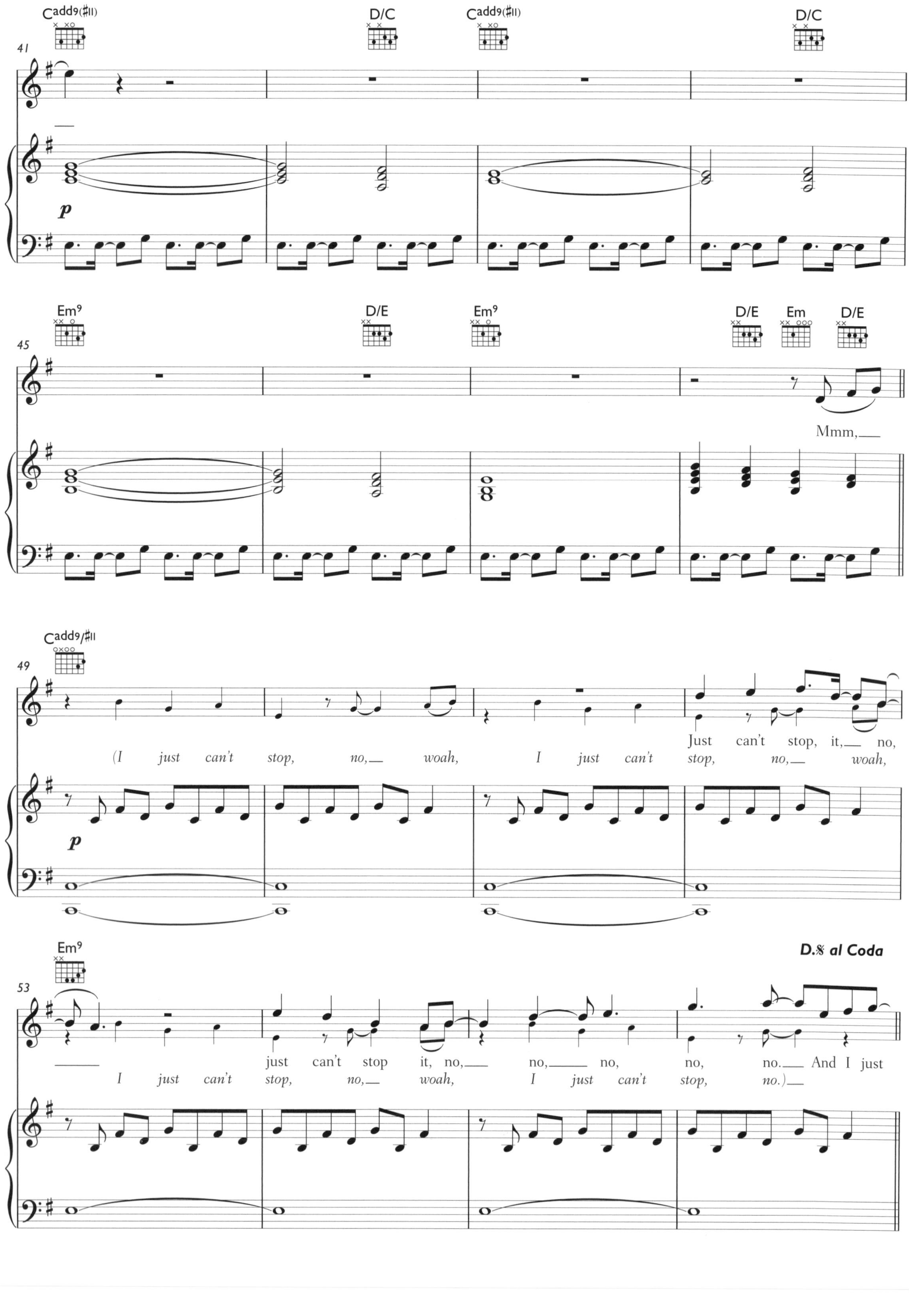
Cadd9(♯11)
D/C
Cadd9(♯11)
D/C
Em9
D/E
Em9
D/E
Em
D/E
Mmm,
Cadd9/♯11
Just can't stop, it, no,
(I just can't stop, no, woah, I just can't stop, no, woah,
Em9
D.% al Coda
just can't stop it, no, no, no, no, no. And I just
I just can't stop, no, woah, I just can't stop, no.)

Coda
Em
D/E
Em
D/E
Cadd9(♯11)
D/C
57
I just… and I just can't pull my - self a - way, un - der a
Cadd9(♯11)
D/C
Em9
D/E
60
spell I can't break, I just can't stop, I just can't stop, I just can't stop,
Em9
D/E
Em
D/E
Cadd9
64
I just can't stop, I just can't stop. Come clos - er…
p

Gnarls Barkley

CRAZY

Words and Music by Thomas Callaway, Brian Burton,
Gianfranco Reverberi and Gian Piero Reverberi

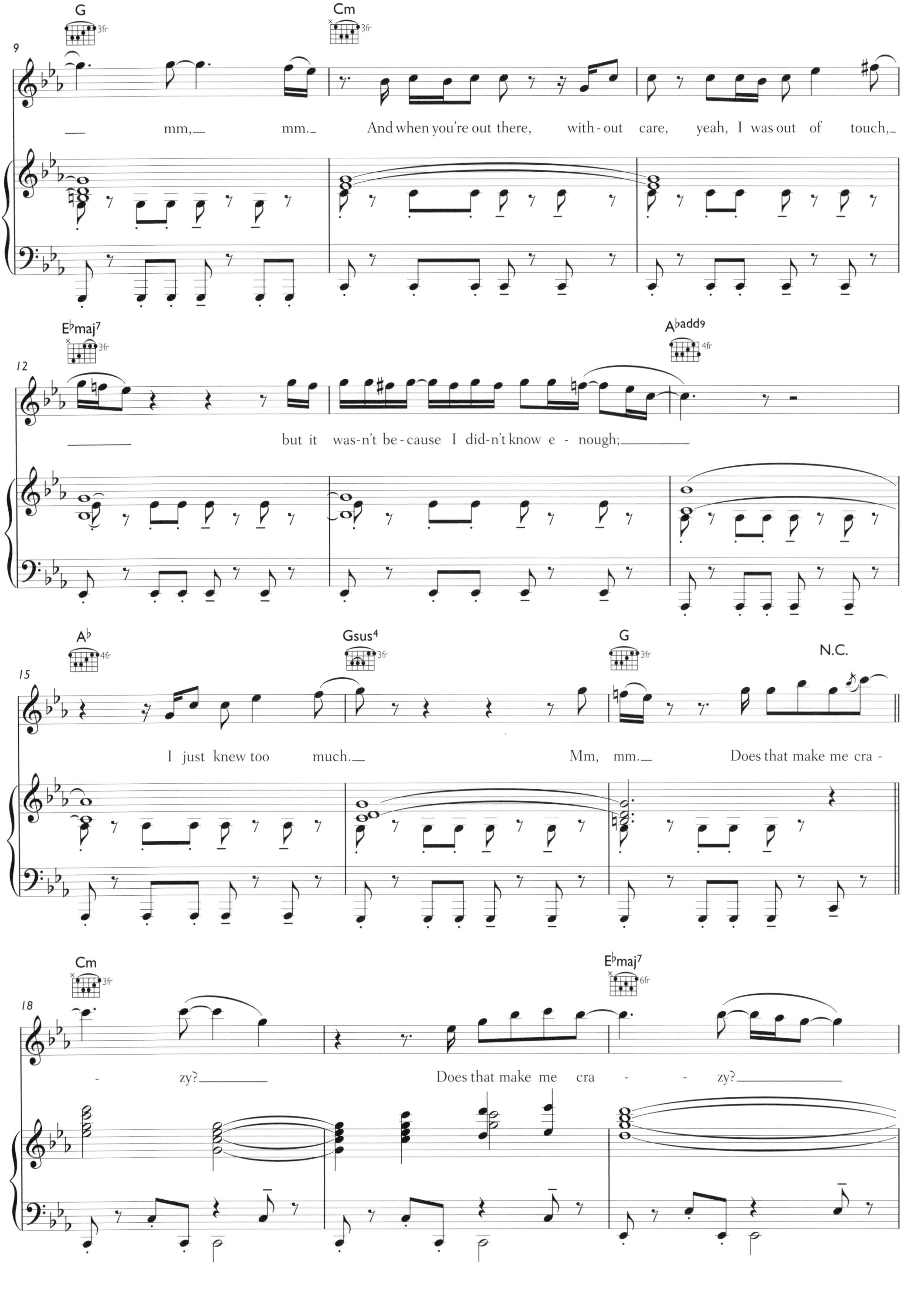
G
Cm
mm, mm. And when you're out there, with-out care, yeah, I was out of touch,
E♭maj7
A♭add9
but it was-n't be-cause I did-n't know e - nough;
A♭
Gsus4
G
N.C.
I just knew too much. Mm, mm. Does that make me cra -
Cm
E♭maj7
- zy? Does that make me cra - - zy?

A♭maj7
8fr
A♭
4fr
21
Does that make me cra - - zy?
Pos - sib - ly.
Gsus4
3fr
G
3fr
C
3fr
24
3
3
2. And I hope that you are hav -
3. My he - roes had the heart
A♭add9
4fr
A♭
4fr
27
- ing the time of your life,
to lose their lives out on a limb,
but think twice;
and all I re - mem -

E♭maj7
Gsus4
30
that's my on - ly ad - vice.
- ber, is think-ing: 'I wan-na be like them.'
G
Cm
33
Mm. Come on now, who do you, who do you, who do you, who do you think you are?
Mm. Ev - er since I was lit - tle, ev - er since I was lit - tle, it looked like fun,
E♭maj7
A♭add9
36
Ha, ha, ha, bless your soul; mm,
and it's no co - in - ci - dence I've come, mm,
A♭
Gsus4
G
N.C.
39
you real - ly think you're in con - trol?
and I can die when I'm done.
Well, I think you're cra -
But may - be I'm cra -

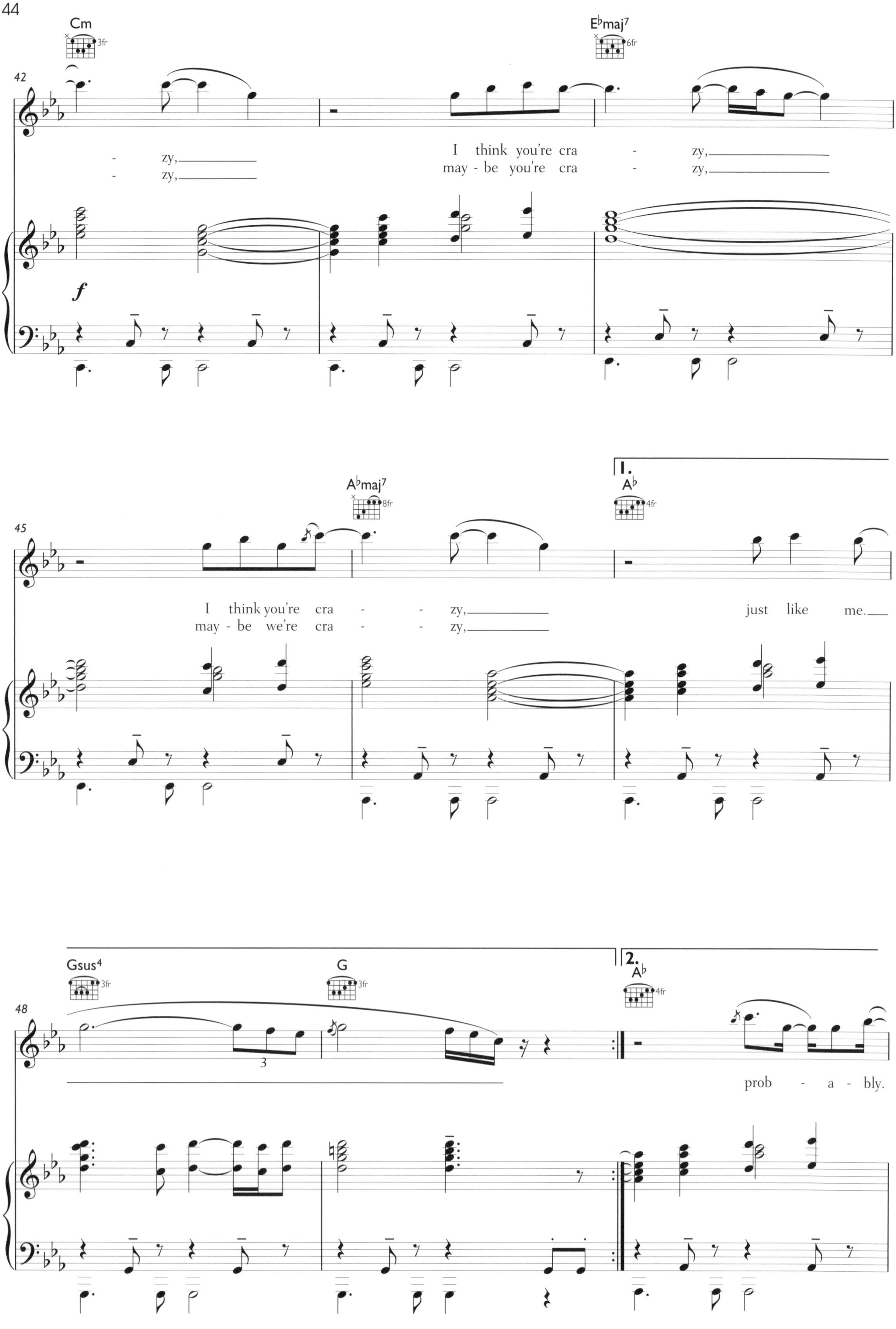
Cm
3fr
E♭maj7
6fr
42
- zy,
- zy,
I think you're cra - zy,
may - be you're cra - zy,
f
A♭maj7
8fr
1.
A♭
4fr
45
I think you're cra - - zy,
may - be we're cra - - zy,
just like me.
Gsus4
3fr
G
3fr
2.
A♭
4fr
48
3
prob - a - bly.

Gsus4
straight ♪s to end
G
51
C
A♭add9
A♭
53
Mm, ah, oo, oo, oo,
mf
E♭maj7
Gsus4
57
woo, oo, oo,
G
C5
60
mm, mm, mm.

DANCING IN THE MOONLIGHT

Words and Music by Sherman Kelly

Fm7
B♭
E♭
B♭/D
Cm7
6fr
3fr
13
- tu - ral de - light, ev - 'ry - bo - dy's danc - ing in the moon -
Fm9
16
- light.
20
2. Ev - 'ry - bo - dy here is out of sight, they don't bark
(3.) and we nev - er fight, you can't dance
23
and they don't bite. They keep things loose, they keep it tight.
and stay up - tight, it's a su - per - na - tu - ral de - light.

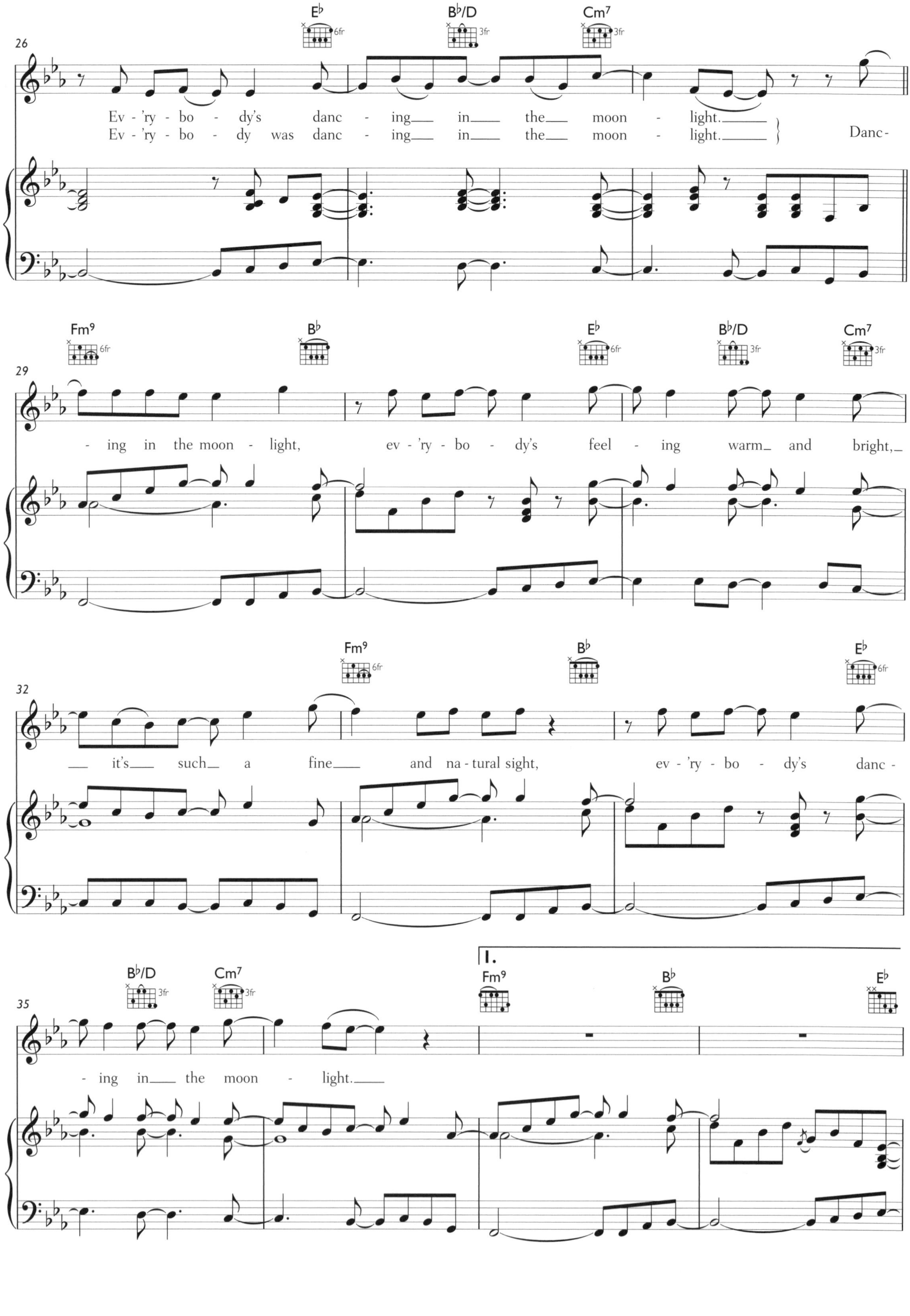

E♭
B♭/D
Cm7
26
Ev - 'ry - bo - dy's danc - ing in the moon - light.
Ev - 'ry - bo - dy was danc - ing in the moon - light.
Danc -
Fm9
B♭
E♭
B♭/D
Cm7
29
- ing in the moon - light, ev - 'ry - bo - dy's feel - ing warm and bright,
Fm9
B♭
E♭
32
it's such a fine and na - tural sight, ev - 'ry - bo - dy's danc -
B♭/D
Cm7
1.
Fm9
B♭
E♭
35
- ing in the moon - light.

2.
B♭/D Cm7 Fm7 B♭sus2 B♭
3. We like our fun
Organ
E♭ B♭/D Cm B♭ Fm7 B♭
E♭ B♭/D Cm Fm7 B♭
We get it on most ev - 'ry night
E♭ B♭/D Cm7
and when that moon is big and bright it's a su - per - na -

Fm7 B♭ E♭ B♭/D Cm7
-tu - ral delight, ev - 'ry - bo - dy's danc - ing in the moon -
Fm9 B♭ E♭
- light. Danc - ing in the moon - light, ev - 'ry - bo - dy's feel-
B♭/D Cm7 Fm9 B♭
- ing warm and bright, it's such a fine and na - tural sight,
E♭ B♭/D Cm7
Repeat ad lib. to fade
ev - 'ry - bo - dy's danc - ing in the moon - light. Danc -

EVERGREEN

Words and Music by David Kreuger,
Per Magnusson and Jorgen Elofsson

C G Dm7 C/E Fadd9 G11
12
don't tell me but it feels like love. I'm gon-na take this
mf f
C G
15
mom - ent and make it last for - ev - er, I'm gon - na give my heart
Fmaj7 G7sus4 G
17
a - way and pray we'll stay to - ge - ther, 'cos you're the one good
C G Dm7
19
rea - son, you're the on - ly girl that I need, 'cos you're more beau - ti - ful than I have ev - er seen,

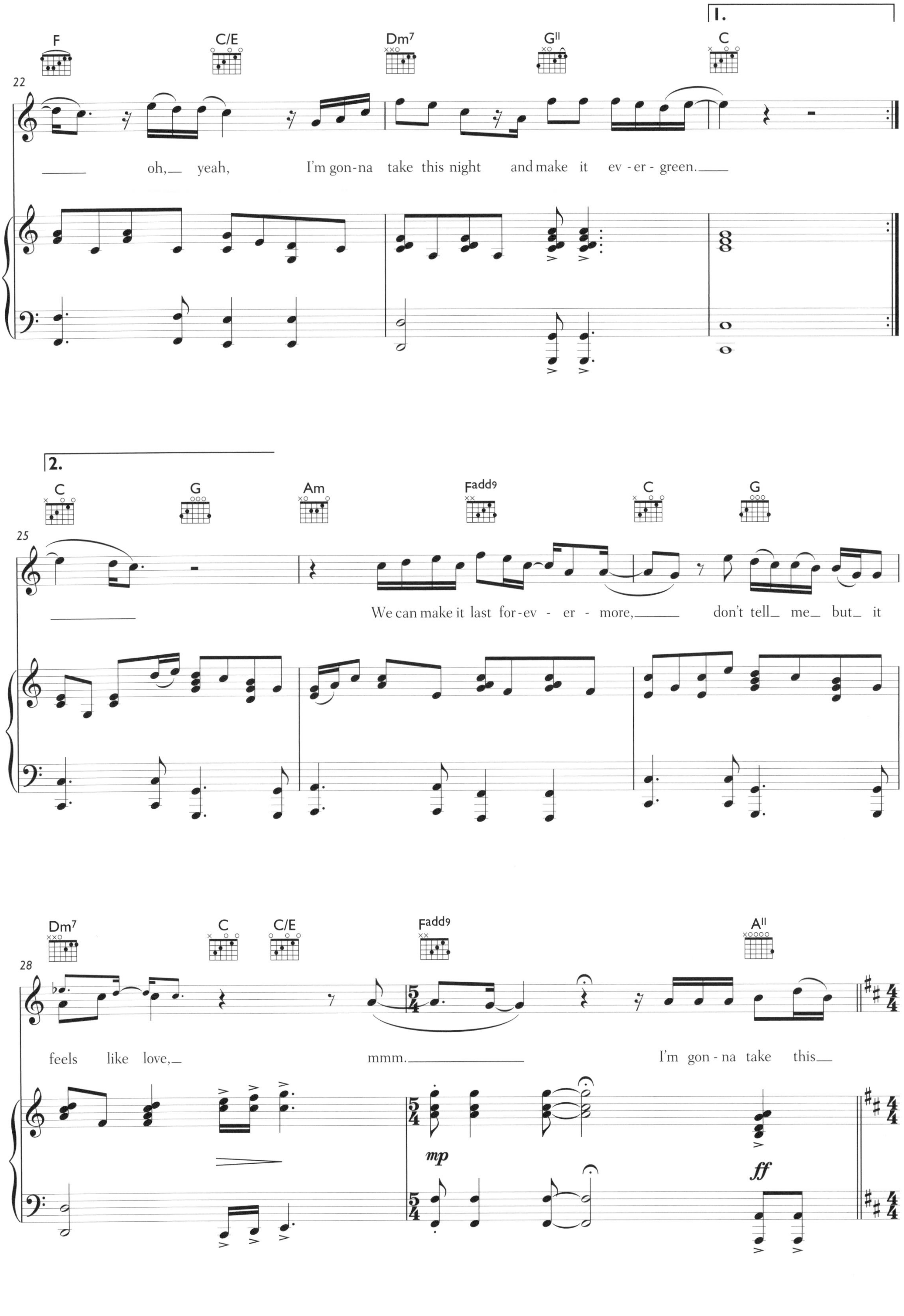
1.
F
C/E
Dm7
G11
C
22
oh, yeah, I'm gon-na take this night and make it ev - er - green.
2.
C
G
Am
Fadd9
C
G
25
We can make it last for-ev - er - more, don't tell me but it
Dm7
C
C/E
Fadd9
A11
28
feels like love, mmm. I'm gon - na take this
mp
ff

30
D
A
mom - ent and make it last for - ev - er, I'm gon - na give my heart
32
Gmaj7
Asus4
A
away and pray we'll stay to - ge - ther, 'cos you're the one good
34
D
A
Asus4
A
rea - son, you're the on - ly girl that I need, 'cos you're more
1.
36
G
Asus4
A
beau - ti - ful than I have ev - er seen, I'm gon - na take this

2.
Em7 D/F♯ G D/F♯
38
beau - ti - ful than I have ev - er seen, ev - er seen, yeah, yeah, I'm gon - na
Em7 A11 D A
40
take this night and make it ev - er - green, oh, yeah,
p
Em7 A11 D
42
yeah, and make it ev - er - green.

FALLIN'

Words and Music by Alicia Augello-Cook

Em
Bm7
Em
Bm7
dar - ling makes me so con - fused. I keep on
fall - in' in and out of love with - a you. I
nev - er loved some - one the way that I love - a you. Oh, oh,
2. I nev - er felt this - a way. How do you give me so much

Em Bm7 Em Bm7
17
pleas - - ure and cause me so much pain? Just when I
Em Bm7 Em Bm7
19
think I've tak-en more than would a fool, I start
4
Em Bm7 Em Bm7
21
fall - - in' back in love with you. I keep on
Em Bm7 Em Bm7
23
fall - in' in and out of love with-a you. I

Em Bm7 Em Bm7
25
nev - er loved some - one the way that I love a - you. Oh ba - by,
Em Bm7 Em Bm7 Em Bm7
27
I, I, I, I'm fall - - in'. I, I, I, I'm
Em Bm7 Em Bm7
30
fall - - - - in'. Fall,
Em Bm7 Em Bm7
32
fall, fall...

Em
Bm7
Em
Bm7
34
I keep on fall - in' in and out of
Em
Bm7
Em
Bm7
36
love with - a you I nev - er loved some - one the way that
Em
Bm7
Em
Bm7
38
I love a - you. I'm fall - in' in and out of
Em
Bm7
Em
Bm7
40
love with - a you. I nev - er loved some - one the way that

Em Bm7 Em Bm7
42
I love a - you. I'm fall - in' in and out of
Em Bm7 Em Bm7
44
love with a - you. I nev - er loved some - one the way that
Em Bm7 N.C. Em Bm7 Em Bm7
46
I love a - you. What?
Em Bm7 Em Bm7 Em
49

FEEL

Words and Music by Robbie Williams and Guy Chambers

Dm/F
A/E
A7
this role I've been giv - en.
I'm pre - par - ing to leave her.
I sit and talk to
I scare my - self to
Dm
C6
A/C♯
God
death,
and he just laughs at my plans.
that's why I keep on run - ning.
A7
Gm
3fr
Dm/F
My head speaks a lan - guage
Be - fore I've ar - rived
I don't un - der - stand.
I can see my - self com -
A/E
A7
B♭
F
- ing.
I just want to feel real love feel the home that I live

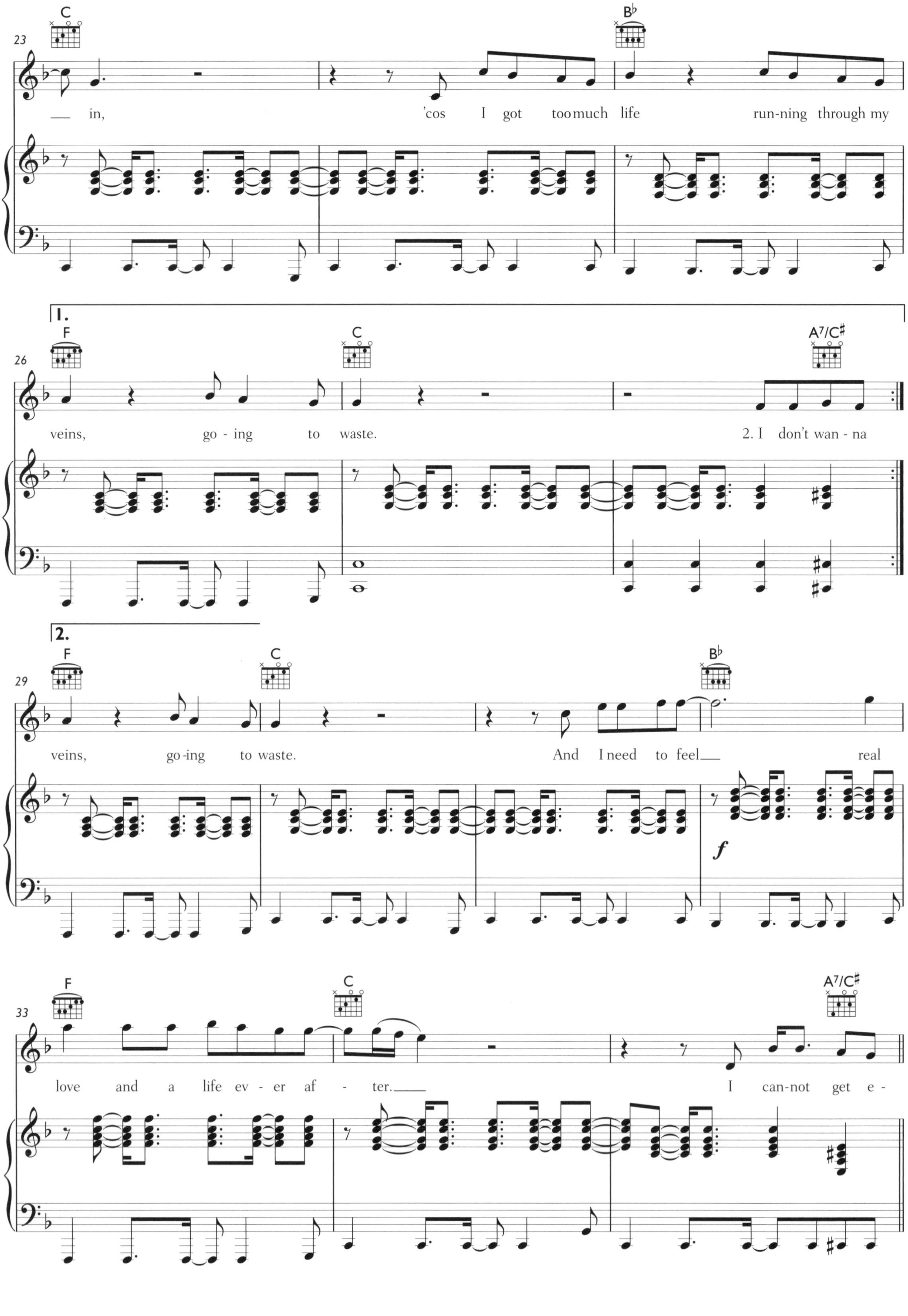

C
B♭
23
— in, 'cos I got too much life run-ning through my
1.
F
C
A7/C♯
26
veins, go - ing to waste. 2. I don't wan - na
2.
F
C
B♭
29
veins, go-ing to waste. And I need to feel — real
f
F
C
A7/C♯
33
love and a life ev - er af - ter. — I can-not get e -

Dm Am/D F/D G/D Dm Am/D F/D G/D
36
- nough.
mp
Dm Am F G Dm Am F G
40
Elec. Gtr.
Dm Am F G Dm Am/E F G
44
I just want to
B♭ F C
48
feel real love feel the home that I live in. I got too much
f

B♭ F C
52
love run-ning through my veins, to go to waste.
I just want to
B♭ F C
56
feel real love and a life ev - er af - ter.
There's a hole in my
B♭ F C A7/C♯
60
soul, you can see it in my face, it's a real big place.
Dm Am/D F/D G/D Dm Am/D F/D G/D
64
Come and hold my
mf

Dm Am F G Dm Am
68
hand, I want to contact the liv - ing.
F G Dm Am F G
71
Not sure I un - der - stand this role I've been giv -
Dm Am/E F G Dm Am
74
- en. Not sure I un - der - stand,
F G Dm Am/E F G Dm7
77
not sure I un - der - stand.

FIGHT FOR THIS LOVE

Words and Music by Stephen Kipner, Wayne Wilkins and Andre Merritt

Play 1° only
G Bm Em Am G
knowing too much can get you hurt. Is it better, is it worse, are we sit-
can't be afraid of the dark. Just know that you're not
D/F♯ G Bm Em
-ting in reverse, it's just like we're going backwards. I know where
Am G D/F♯ G Bm
I want this to go, driving fast but let's go slow, what I don't wanna do is crash,
Em Am G D/F♯
no. Just know that you're not in this thing alone. There's always a place
* play both times

G Bm Em Em9 Am G
23
in me that you can call home. When-ev-er you feel like we're grow - ing a - part,
D G D Em
26
let's just go back, back, back, back, back to the start, oh.
Am G D/F♯ G D Em
29
A - ny-thing that's worth hav - ing is sure e - nough worth fight - ing for.
Am G D G Bm Em
33
Quit-ting's out of the ques - tion, when it gets tough, got - ta fight some more. We got - ta

Am G D/F# G D Em
37
fight, fight, fight, fight, fight for this love, we got-ta fight, fight, fight, fight, fight for this love. We got-ta
To Coda
Am G D G Bm7 Em
41
(2° only)
fight, fight, fight, fight, fight for this love, if it's worth hav-ing it's worth fight-ing for. I don't know
Am G D C G D/F#
45
where we're head-ing, I'm will-ing and rea-dy to go. We've been dri-
mp
Am G D C G D/F#
49
-ving so fast, we just need to slow down and just roll, oh.

53
N.C.
A - ny-thing that's worth hav - ing is sure e - nough worth fight - ing for.
57
D.𝄋 al Coda
Quit-ting's out of the ques - tion, when it gets tough, got - ta fight some more. We got - ta
𝄌 Coda
61
Em Am G D/F♯ G D
(for.) We got-ta fight, fight, fight, fight, fight for this love, we got-ta fight, fight, fight, fight,
f
65
Em Am G D G Bm7
fight for this love. We got-ta fight, fight, fight, fight, fight for this love, if it's worth hav-ing it's worth fight - ing for,
69
Em Am G D/F♯ G D Em
Repeat & fade
oh.

HANDBAGS AND GLADRAGS

Words and Music by Mike D'Abo

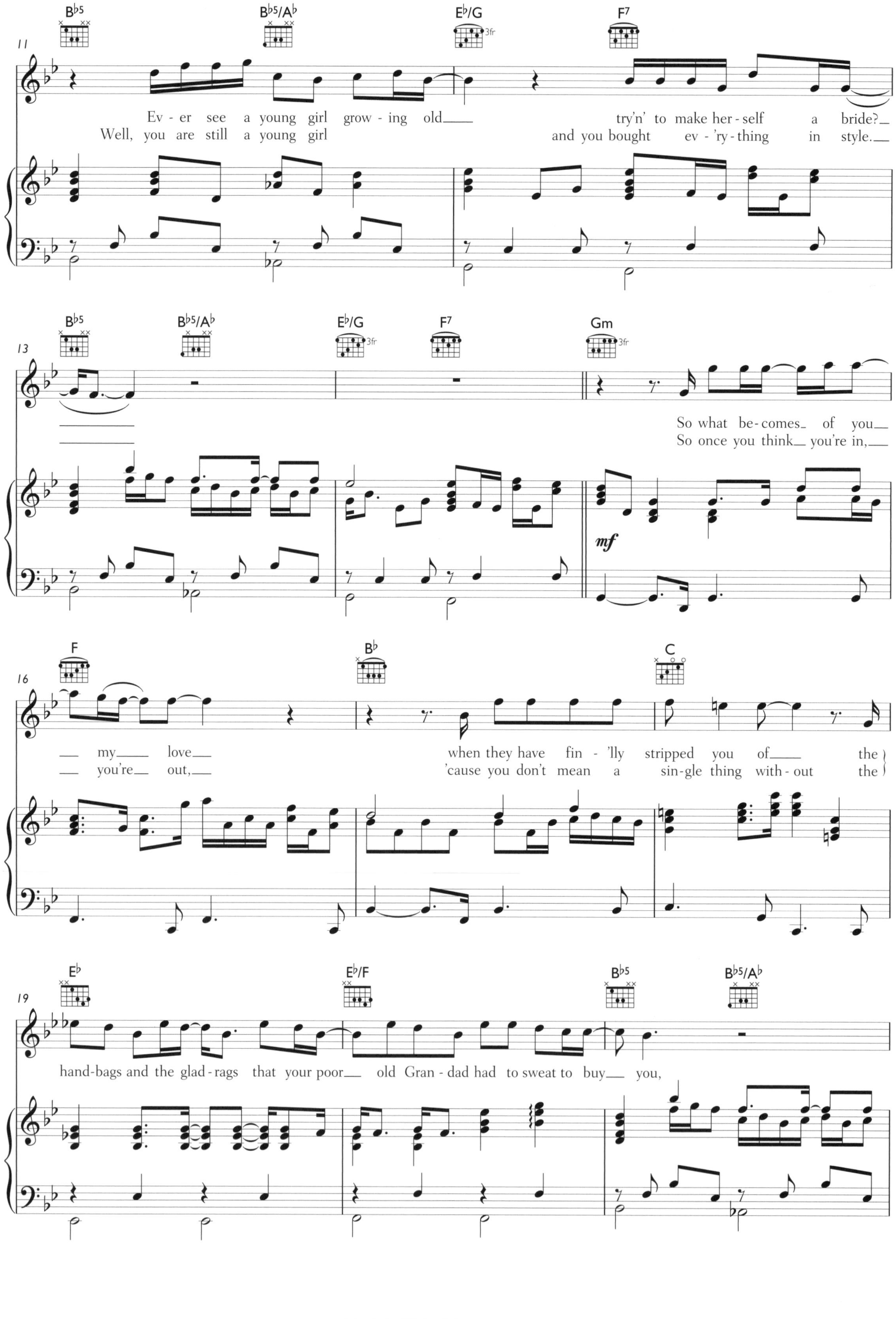
B♭5 B♭5/A♭ E♭/G F7
11
Ev - er see a young girl grow - ing old try'n' to make her - self a bride?
Well, you are still a young girl and you bought ev - 'ry - thing in style.
B♭5 B♭5/A♭ E♭/G F7 Gm
13
So what be - comes of you
So once you think you're in,
mf
F B♭ C
16
my love when they have fin - 'lly stripped you of the
you're out, 'cause you don't mean a sin-gle thing with - out the
E♭ E♭/F B♭5 B♭5/A♭
19
hand-bags and the glad - rags that your poor old Gran - dad had to sweat to buy you,

1.
2.
22
E♭/G F7 B♭5 B♭5/A♭ E♭/G F7
3fr
yeah, yeah.
25
E♭/G F7 B♭ E♭/F B♭ B♭/A♭
mp
Sing a song of six-pence for your sake
28
E♭/G F7 B♭ B♭/A♭ E♭/G F7
and drink a bot-tle full of rye.
31
B♭ B♭/A♭ E♭/G F7 B♭ B♭/A♭
Four and twen-ty black-birds in a cake and bake them all in a pie.

E♭/G
F7
Gm
3fr
F
34
They told me you missed school to - day,
f
B♭
C
E♭
37
so what I sug-gest you just throw them all a- way,
the hand-bags and the glad-rags that your poor
E♭/F
N.C.
40
old Gran-dad had to sweat to buy you, woh, woh.
Gm
43
They told me you missed
mp

F
B♭
C
46
school_ to - day,_ so what I sug-gest you just throw them all__ a - way,_ the
E♭
E♭/F
B♭5
B♭5/A♭
49
hand-bags and the glad - rags that your poor__ old Gran-dad had to sweat to buy__ you.
f
E♭/G
F7
B♭5
B♭5/A♭
3fr
52
56
rit.
E♭/G
E♭/F
B♭

Michael Bublé

HAVEN'T MET YOU YET

Words and Music by Michael Bublé, Alan Chang and Amy Foster-Gillies

G♭maj7
E♭m7
A♭
Daug
in, I talked my-self out, I get all worked up then I let my-self down.
when-e-ver it's right, you'll come out of no-where and in-to my life.
E♭m7
D♭/F
E♭m7
I tried so ve-ry hard not to lose it, I came up with a
And I know that we can be so a-ma-zing, and ba-by, your
A♭
E♭m7
D♭/F
mil-li-on ex-cu-ses. I thought I thought of ev-'ry pos-si-bi-li-ty.
love is gon-na change me. And now I can see ev-'ry pos-si-bi-li-ty.
G♭
A♭
G♭
A♭
And I know some day
And some-how I know
that it-'ll all turn out,

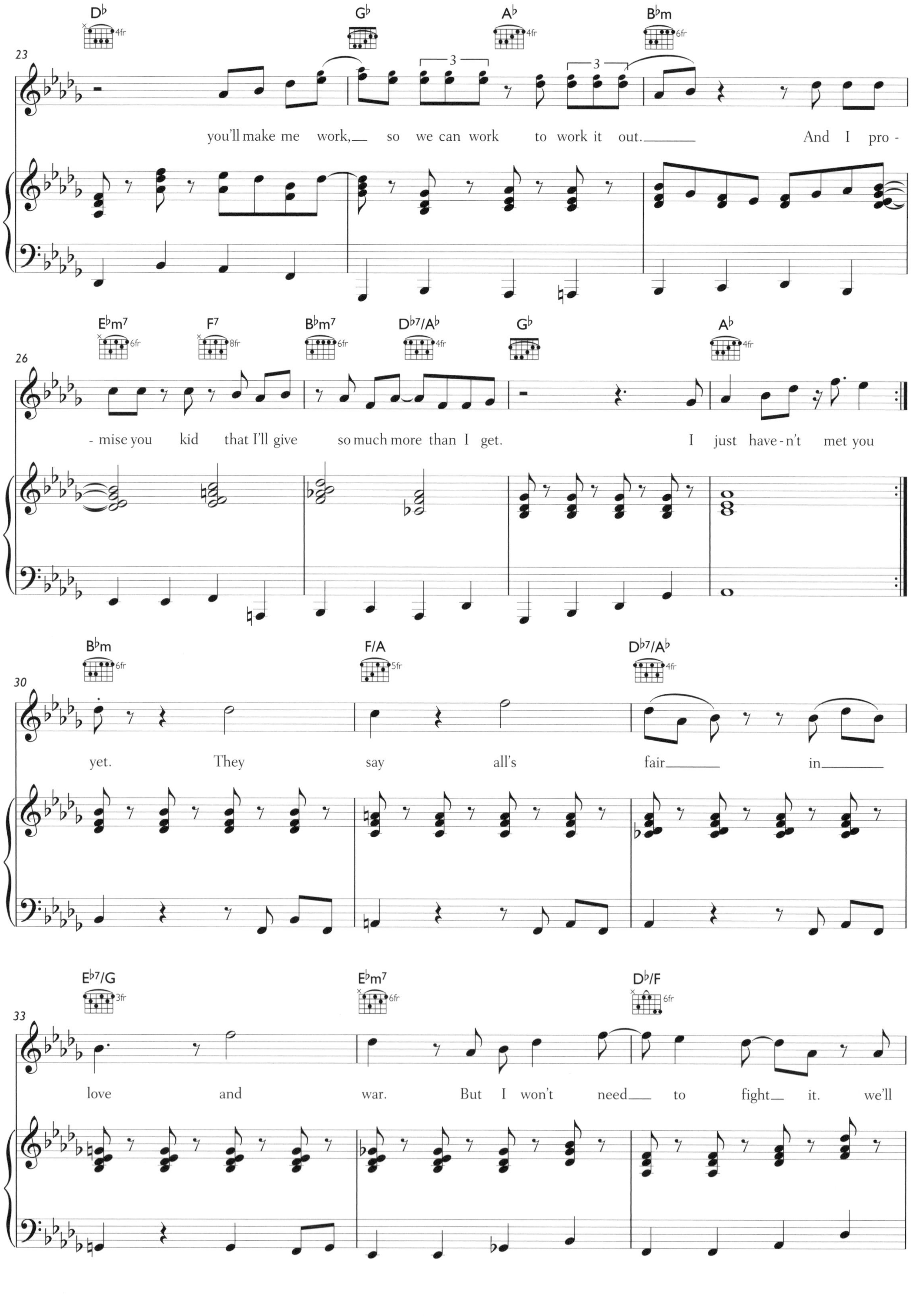
Db
4fr
Gb
Ab
4fr
Bbm
6fr
23
3
3
you'll make me work, so we can work to work it out. And I pro -
Ebm7
6fr
F7
8fr
Bbm7
6fr
Db7/Ab
4fr
Gb
Ab
4fr
26
- mise you kid that I'll give so much more than I get. I just have-n't met you
Bbm
6fr
F/A
5fr
Db7/Ab
4fr
30
yet. They say all's fair in
Eb7/G
3fr
Ebm7
6fr
Db/F
6fr
33
love and war. But I won't need to fight it. we'll

G♭
A♭
36
get it right and we'll be u - ni - ted.
A♭maj7
B♭
E♭
A♭maj7
B♭
Cm
39
A♭
G7
Cm
E♭7/B♭
A♭
B♭
43
Fm11
E♭/G
Fm11
47
And I know that we can be so a - ma - zing,
and be - ing in your
mf

Fm11
E♭/G
50
life is gon - na change me, and now I can see ev - 'ry sin - gle pos -
A♭add9
B♭
53
- si - bi - li - ty, mmm. And some - day I
A♭maj7
B♭
E♭
A♭maj7
B♭
Cm
56
know it - 'll all turn out, and I'll work to work it out.
mp
A♭
G7
Cm
E♭7/B♭
A♭
60
Pro - mise you kid, I'll give more than I get, than I get,

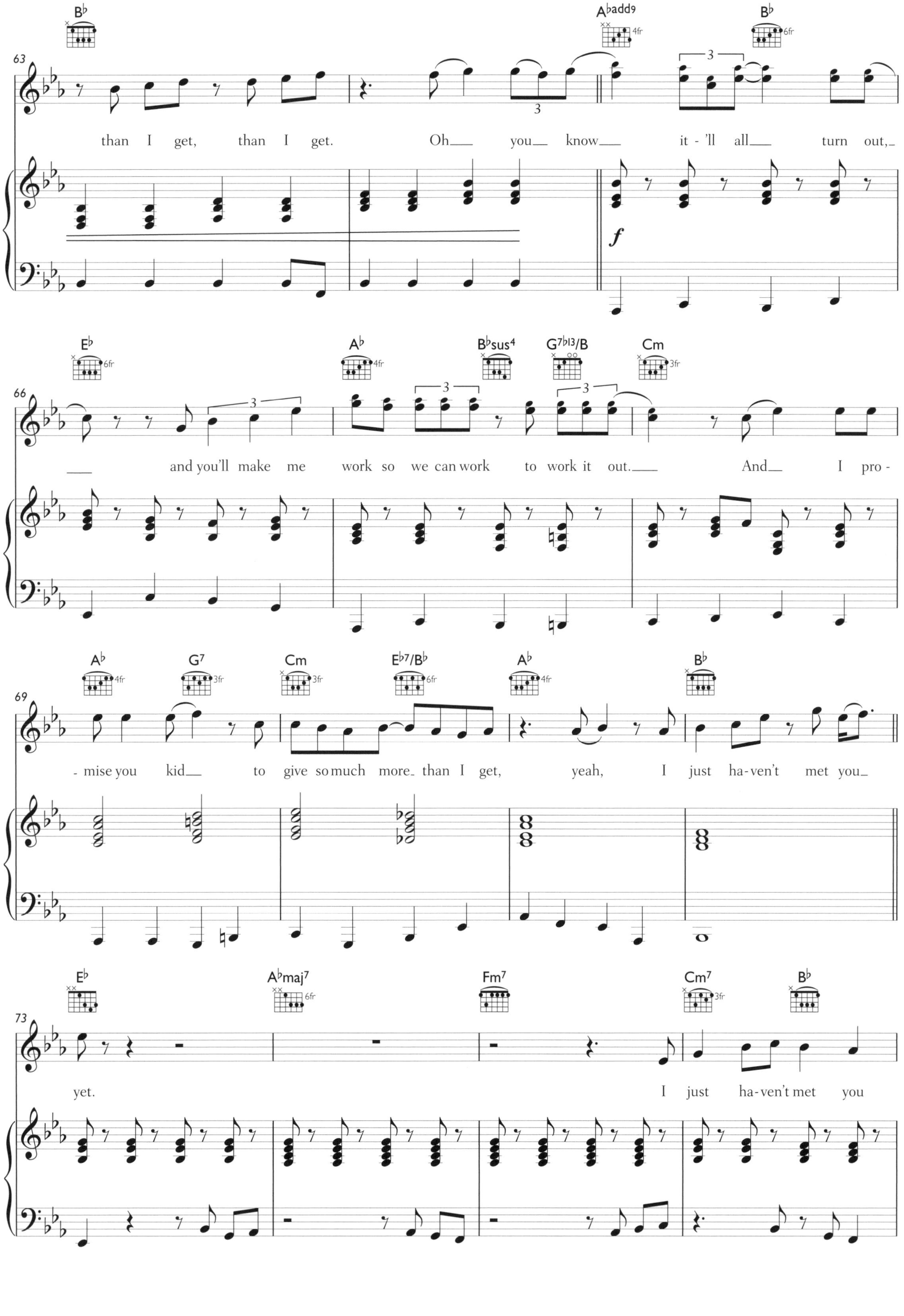
B♭
A♭add9
B♭
than I get, than I get. Oh you know it-'ll all turn out,
E♭
A♭
B♭sus4
G7♭13/B
Cm
and you'll make me work so we can work to work it out. And I pro-
A♭
G7
Cm
E♭7/B♭
A♭
B♭
-mise you kid to give so much more than I get, yeah, I just ha-ven't met you
E♭
A♭maj7
Fm7
Cm7
B♭
yet. I just ha-ven't met you

E♭
A♭maj7
Fm7
77
yet. Oh, pro-mise you kid to give so much more than I get.
Cm7
B♭
E♭
A♭maj7
Fm7
80
I said love, love, love, love. Love, love,
I
Cm7
B♭
E♭
A♭maj7
84
love, love. Love, love, love, love.
just ha-ven't met you yet.
Fm7
Cm7
B♭
E♭
87
I just ha-ven't met you yet.

HERO

Words and Music by Enrique Iglesias,
Paul Barry and Mark Taylor

Moderate Ballad

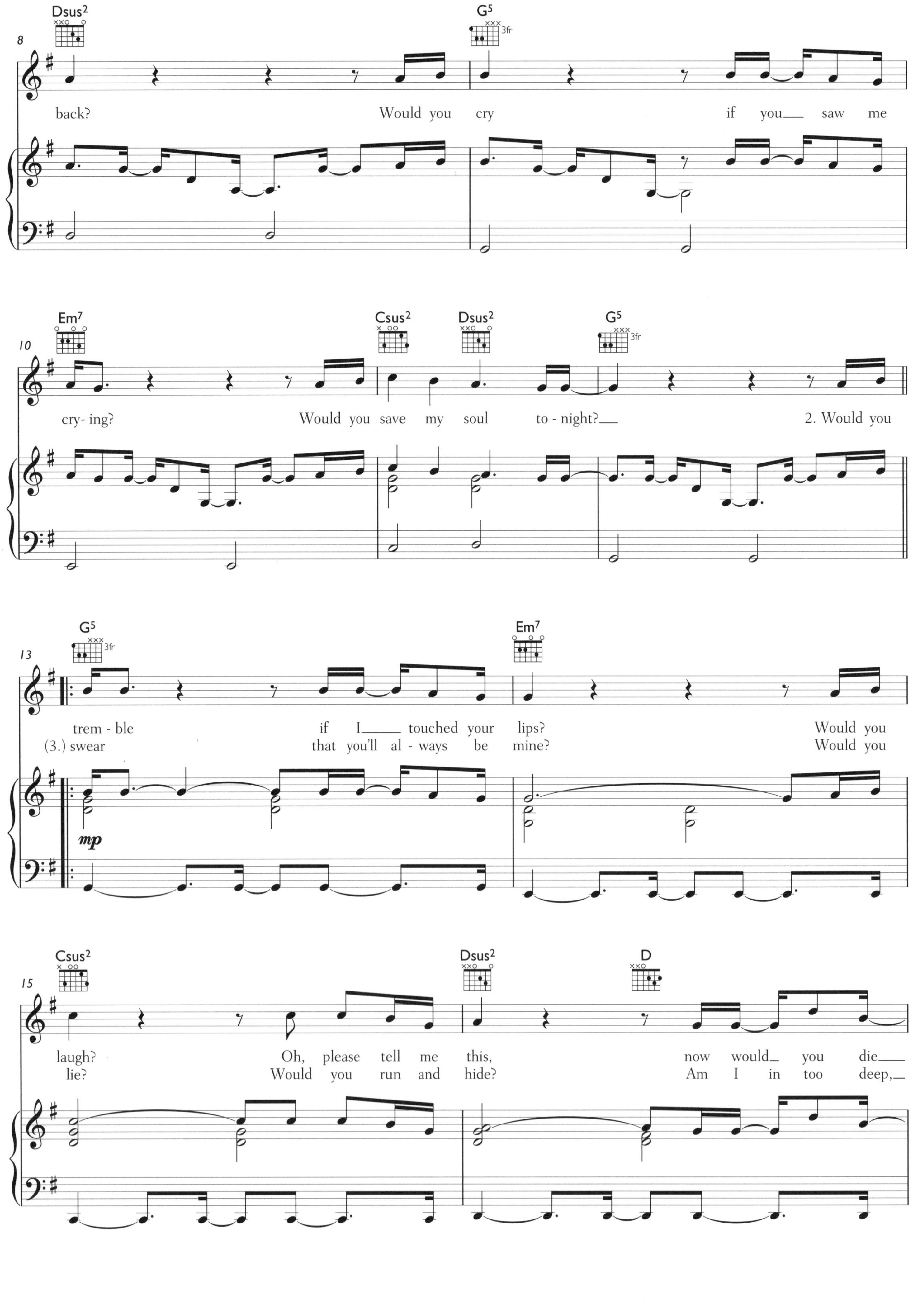
Dsus2
G5
3fr
8
back? Would you cry if you saw me
Em7
Csus2
Dsus2
G5
3fr
10
cry- ing? Would you save my soul to - night?
2. Would you
G5
3fr
Em7
13
trem - ble if I touched your lips? Would you
(3.) swear that you'll al - ways be mine? Would you
mp
Csus2
Dsus2
D
15
laugh? Oh, please tell me this, now would you die
lie? Would you run and hide? Am I in too deep,

G5
Em7
Csus2
Dsus2
17
for the one you love?
Hold me in your arms to-night.
have I lost my mind?
I don't care, you're here to-night.
G5
G
D
Csus2
D/F♯
20
I can be your he-ro ba-by,
mf
G
Dsus4
Csus2
D/F♯
23
I can kiss a-way the pain,
To Coda
G
D
Csus2
D/F♯
25
I will stand by you for-ev-er,

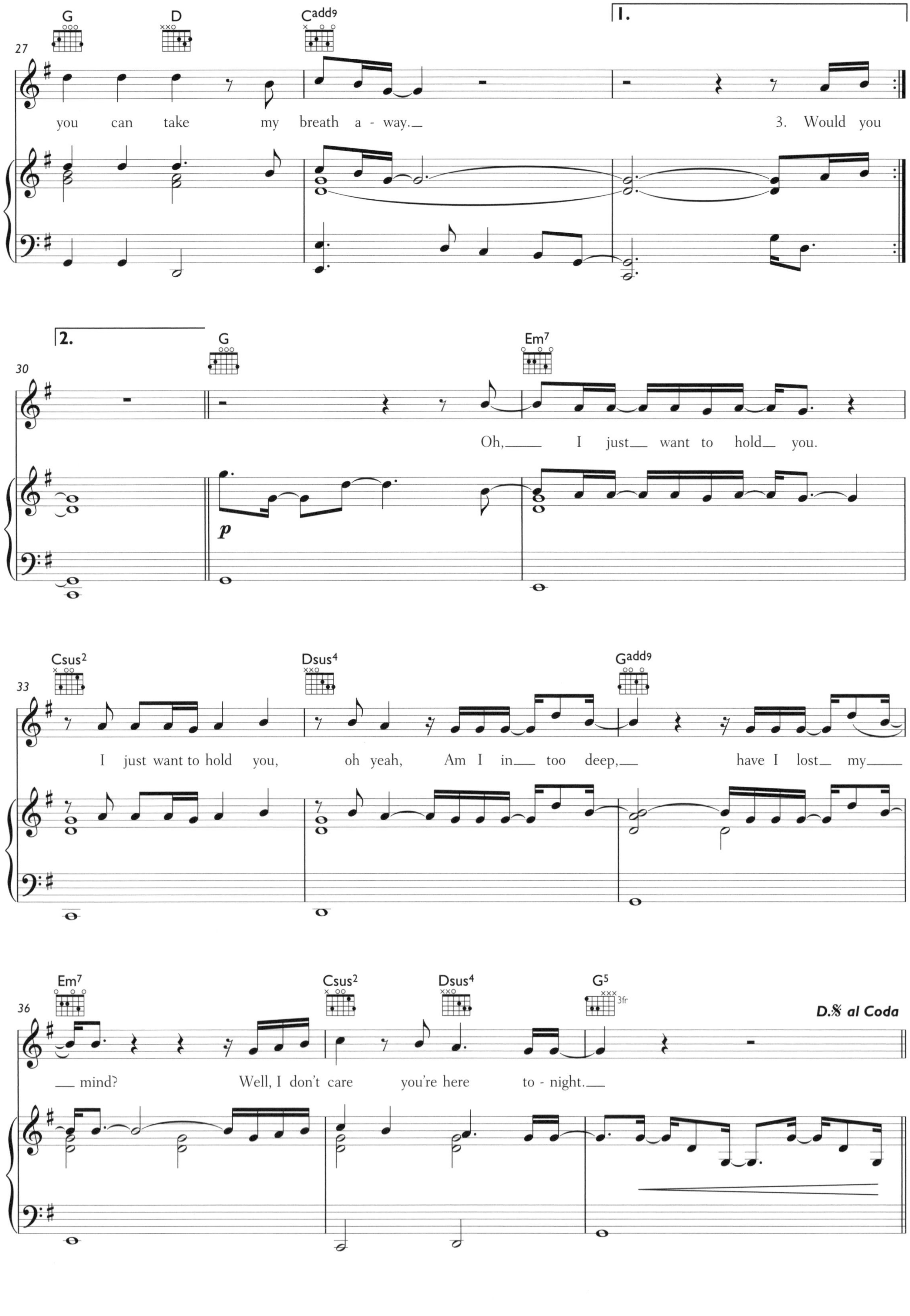
G D Cadd9
1.
27
you can take my breath a - way.
3. Would you
2.
G Em7
30
Oh, I just want to hold you.
p
Csus2 Dsus4 Gadd9
33
I just want to hold you, oh yeah, Am I in too deep, have I lost my
Em7 Csus2 Dsus4 G5
3fr
D.𝄋 al Coda
36
mind? Well, I don't care you're here to - night.

Coda
G D Cadd9 C/E D
you can take my breath a - way.
I can be your he - ro ba -
Csus2 C/E D/F♯ G Dsus4 Csus2 C/E D/F♯
- by, I can kiss a - way the pain, and I will
G D Csus2 C/E D/F♯ G D
stand by you for - ev - er, you can take my
Csus2 G D Csus2
breath a - way. I can be your he - ro.
mp

I DON'T FEEL LIKE DANCIN'

Words and Music by Scott Hoffman, Jason Sellards and Elton John

13
D G/D D Em/D D
1. Wake up in the morn - ing with a head like, 'What you done?' This
2. Cit - ies come and cit - ies go just like the old em-pires, when
15
G C/G G Gsus2/4 G
used to be the life, but I don't need an - oth - er one.
all you do is change your clothes and call that ver - sa - tile. You
17
D G/D D Em/D D
You like cut - ting up and car - ry'n' on, you wear them gowns, so
got so man - y col - ours, it'd make a blind man so con - fused, so
19
G C/G G Gsus2/4 G
how come I feel so lone - ly when you're up get - ting down? So I'll
why can't I keep up when you're the on - ly thing I'd lose? So I'll

Bm
21
F♯m
— play a - long — when I hear — that spe - cial song, —
— just pre - tend — that I know — which way to bend, —
Am
23
G
I'm gon - na be the one — that gets it right. —
I'm gon - na tell the whole — world that you're mine. —
Bm
25
F♯m
You'd bet - ter move — when you're swing - ing 'round the room, —
Please un - der - stand — when I see — you clap your hands, — if
Am
27
G
looks like the mag - ic's on - ly ours — to - night. —
you stick a - round I'm sure that I'll be fine. —
But I —

D G/D D Em/D D
— don't feel like danc - in' when the old — Jo - an - na plays, — my heart —
G C/G G Gsus2/4 G
— could take a chance but my — two feet can't find a way. — You'd think that I —
A C7 G C/G G
— could mus - ter up — a lit - tle soft — shoe gen - tle sway, — but I —
D G/D D G/D D
— don't feel like danc - in', no sir, no danc - in' to - day. — I don't feel like

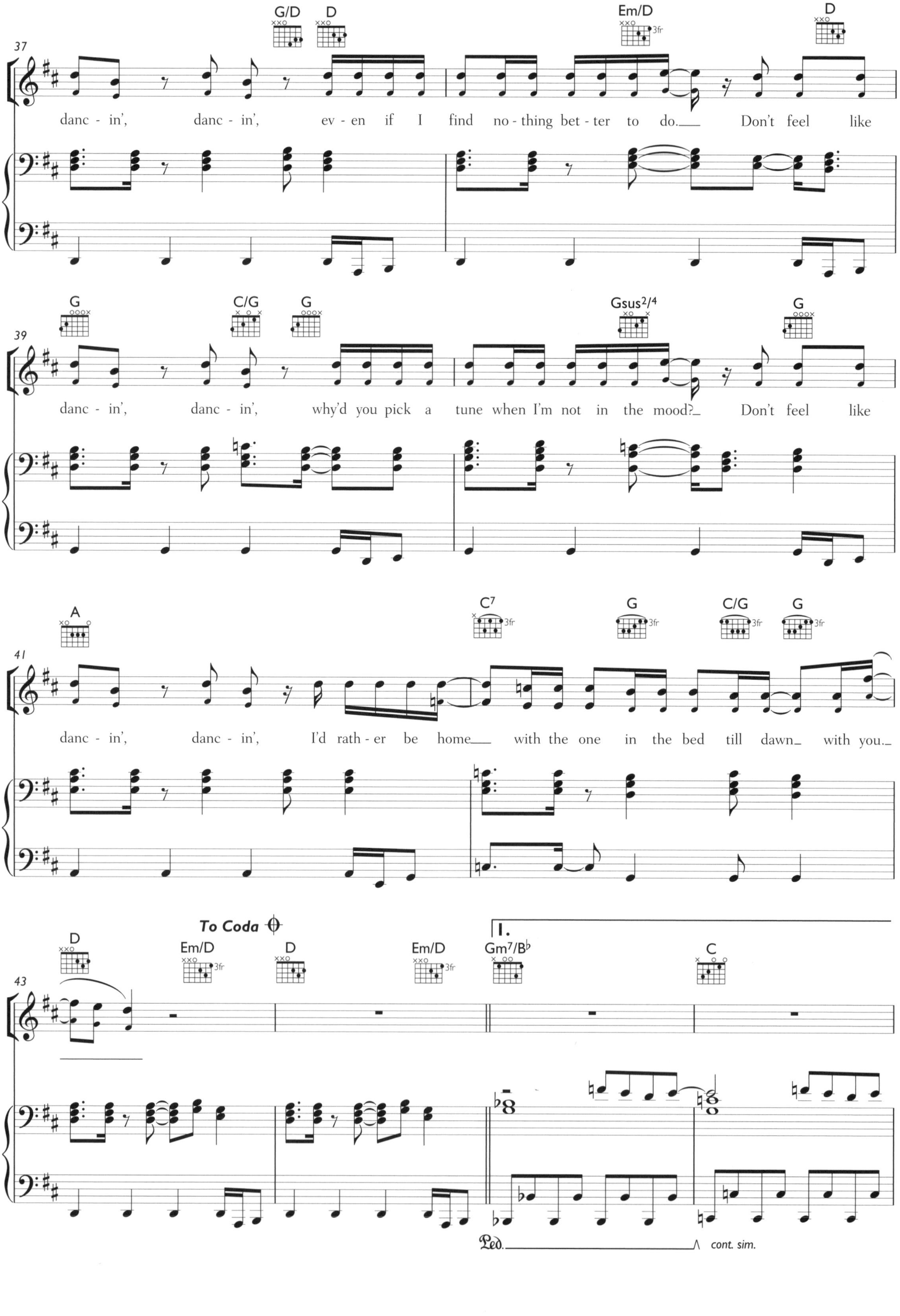
37
G/D D Em/D 3fr D
danc - in', danc - in', ev - en if I find no - thing bet - ter to do. Don't feel like
39
G C/G G Gsus2/4 G
danc - in', danc - in', why'd you pick a tune when I'm not in the mood? Don't feel like
41
A C7 3fr G 3fr C/G 3fr G 3fr
danc - in', danc - in', I'd rath - er be home with the one in the bed till dawn with you.
To Coda
43
D Em/D 3fr D Em/D 3fr Gm7/B♭ C
1.
Ped. cont. sim.

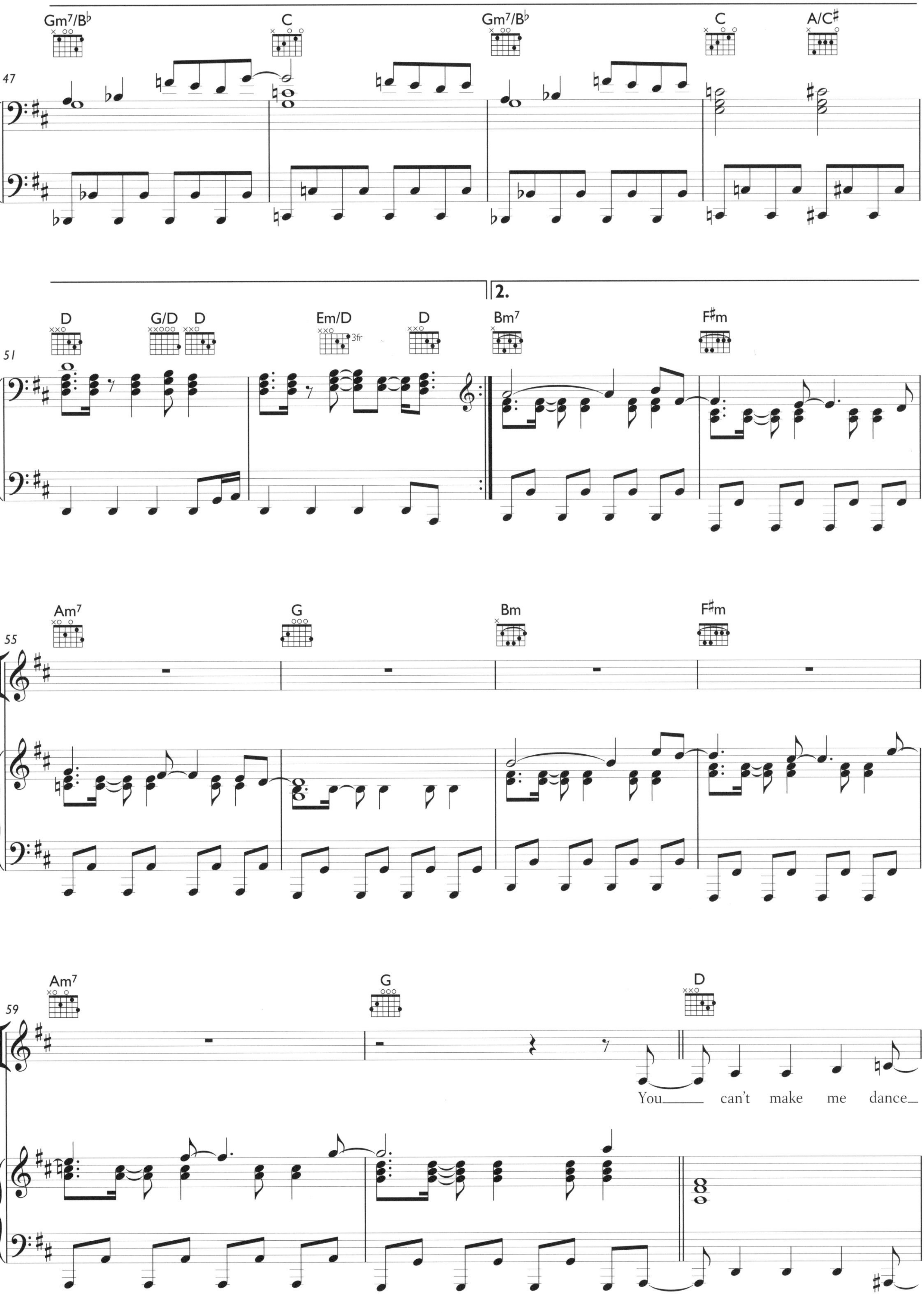

You___ can't make me dance___

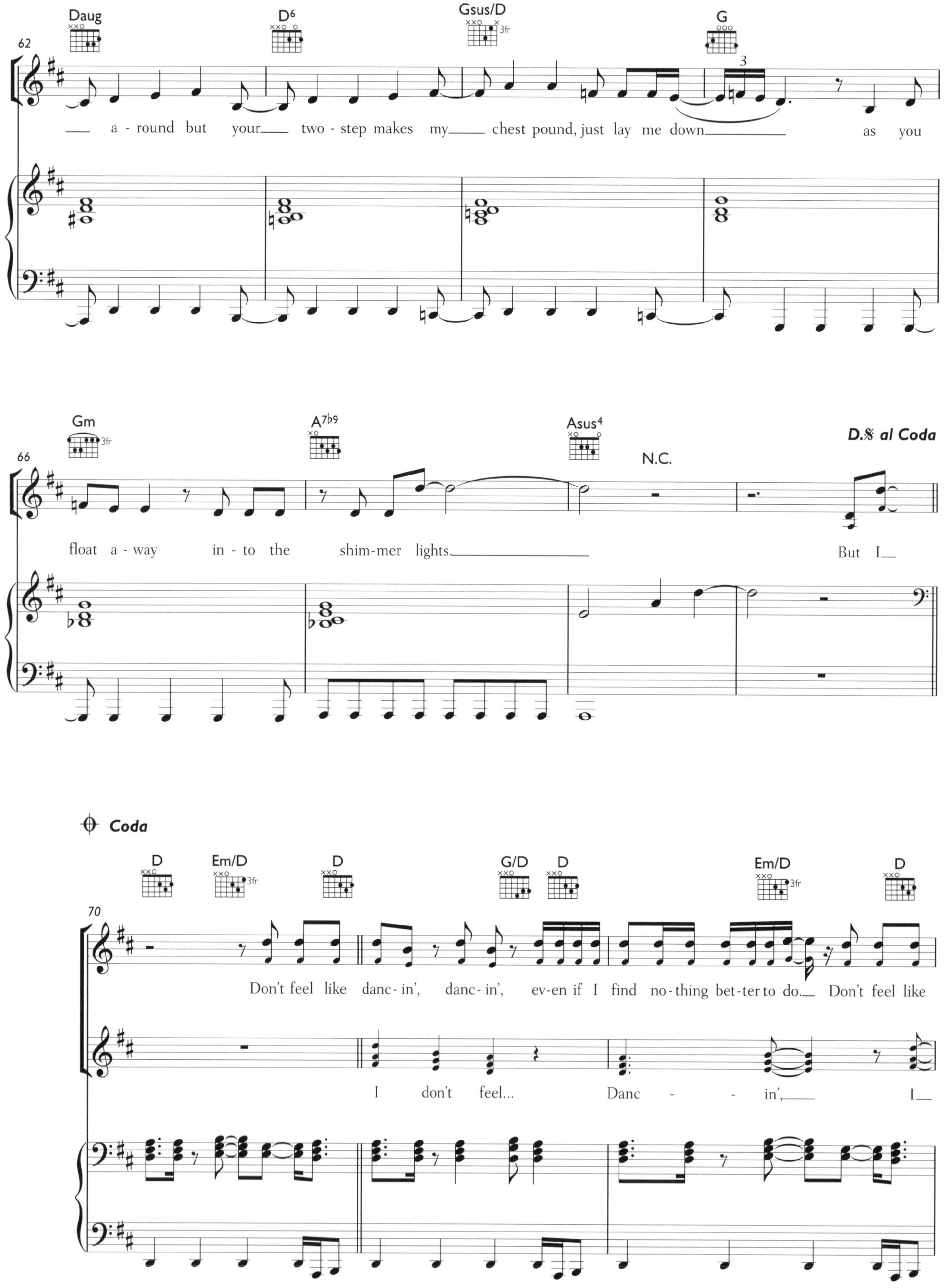

Daug D6 Gsus/D G
62
3
a - round but your two - step makes my chest pound, just lay me down as you
Gm A7♭9 Asus4
D.𝄋 al Coda
66
N.C.
float a - way in - to the shim-mer lights But I
Coda
D Em/D D G/D D Em/D D
70
Don't feel like danc - in', danc - in', ev - en if I find no - thing bet - ter to do. Don't feel like
I don't feel... Danc - in', I

G C/G G Gsus2/4 G A
73
danc-in', danc-in', why'd you pick a tune when I'm not in the mood? Don't feel like danc-in', danc-in' I'd rath-er be home
don't feel... Danc - in', I don't feel...
C7 G C/G G D Em/D D Em/D D
3fr
76
with the one in the bed till dawn with you.
Danc - in' with - out you.
G/D D Em/D D G/D D Em/D D
79

IF THERE'S ANY JUSTICE

Words and Music by Mick Leeson and Peter Vale

F♯m
F♯m(maj7)
F♯m7
9fr
5fr
12
1,3. If there's an - y jus - tice in the world, I would be your
2. If there's an - y jus - tice in your heart, your love real - ly changed,
mp
D
A
C♯aug7
14
man, you would be my girl, oh, yeah,
ease it in - to heart, oh, no,
16
if I found you first you know it's true, he would be a - lone, I would be with
why don't you re - mem-ber how it feels not to give a damn for an - y - one but
19
you.
me?
C♯sus4
When you de - cide,
I can't be - lieve
mf

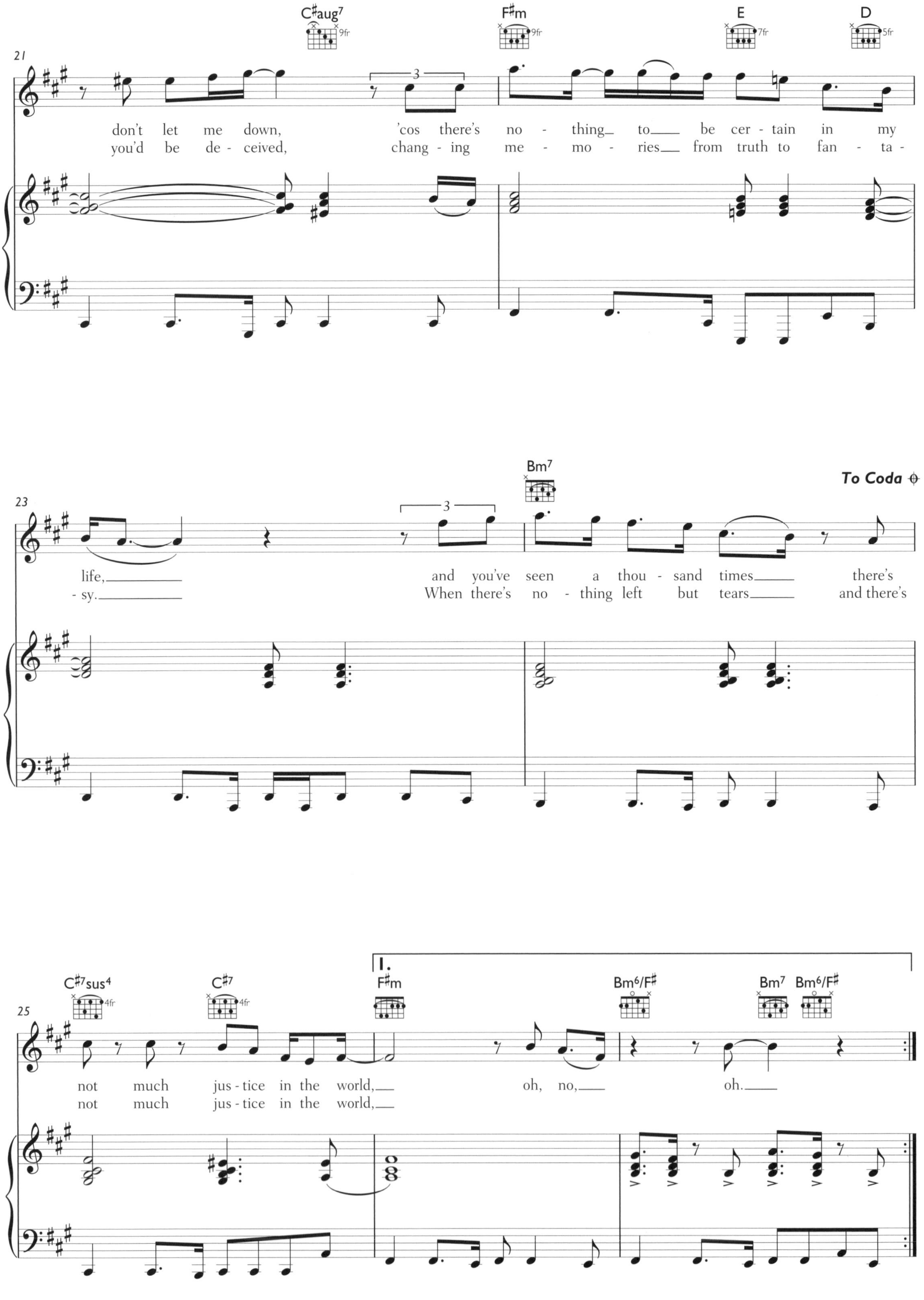
C♯aug7
F♯m
E
D
don't let me down, 'cos there's no - thing to be cer - tain in my
you'd be de - ceived, chang - ing me - mo - ries from truth to fan - ta -
Bm7
To Coda ⊕
life, and you've seen a thou - sand times there's
- sy. When there's no - thing left but tears and there's
C♯7sus4
C♯7
1.
F♯m
Bm6/F♯
Bm7
Bm6/F♯
not much jus - tice in the world, oh, no, oh.
not much jus - tice in the world,

2.
F♯m
9fr
D
5fr
A
5fr
28
oh.
Just be - cause he's wrapped a - round_ your
f
C♯7
4fr
30
fing - er, don't fool your - self_ with dreams that_ might ap -
F♯m
D
5fr
A
5fr
32
- pear, oh,_ ev - 'ry time you stop and trust_ your

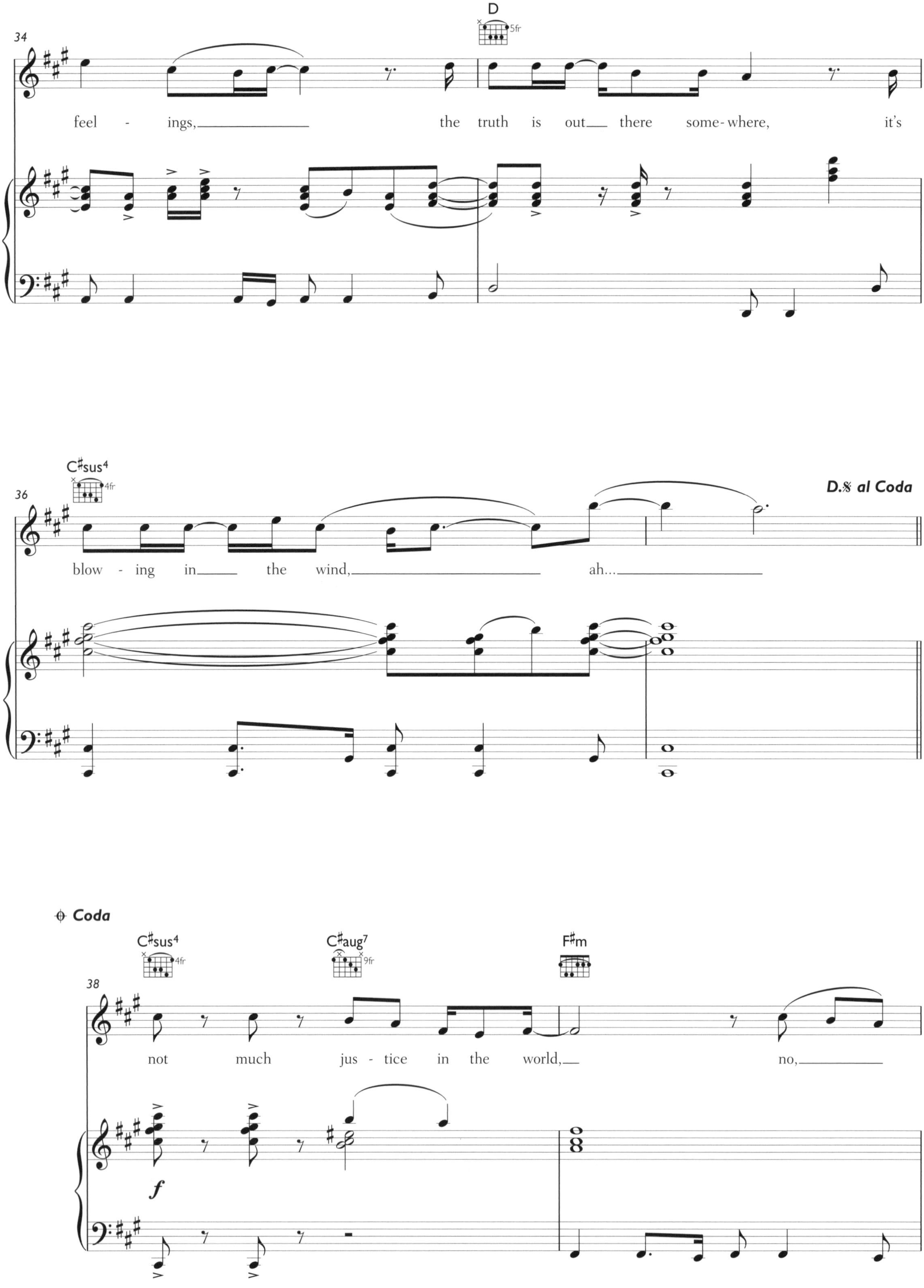
34
D
5fr
feel - ings, the truth is out there some-where, it's
C♯sus4
4fr
36
D.𝄋 al Coda
blow - ing in the wind, ah...
𝄌 Coda
C♯sus4
4fr
C♯aug7
9fr
F♯m
38
not much jus - tice in the world, no,
f

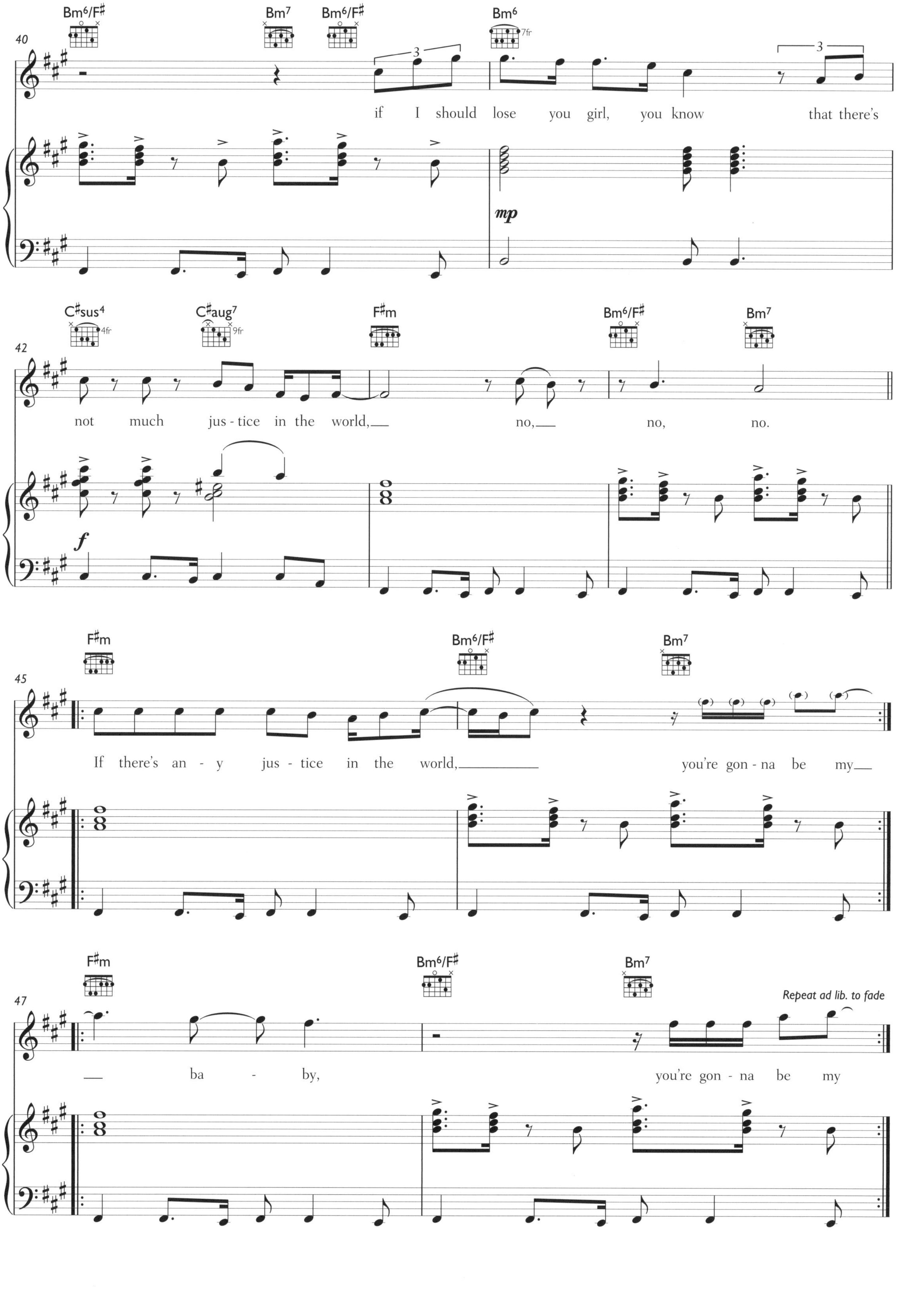
Bm6/F♯
Bm7
Bm6/F♯
Bm6
7fr
40
if I should lose you girl, you know that there's
mp
C♯sus4
4fr
C♯aug7
9fr
F♯m
Bm6/F♯
Bm7
42
not much jus - tice in the world, no, no, no.
f
F♯m
Bm6/F♯
Bm7
45
If there's an - y jus - tice in the world, you're gon - na be my
F♯m
Bm6/F♯
Bm7
47
Repeat ad lib. to fade
ba - by, you're gon - na be my

I'D RATHER BE WITH YOU

Words and Music by Joshua Radin

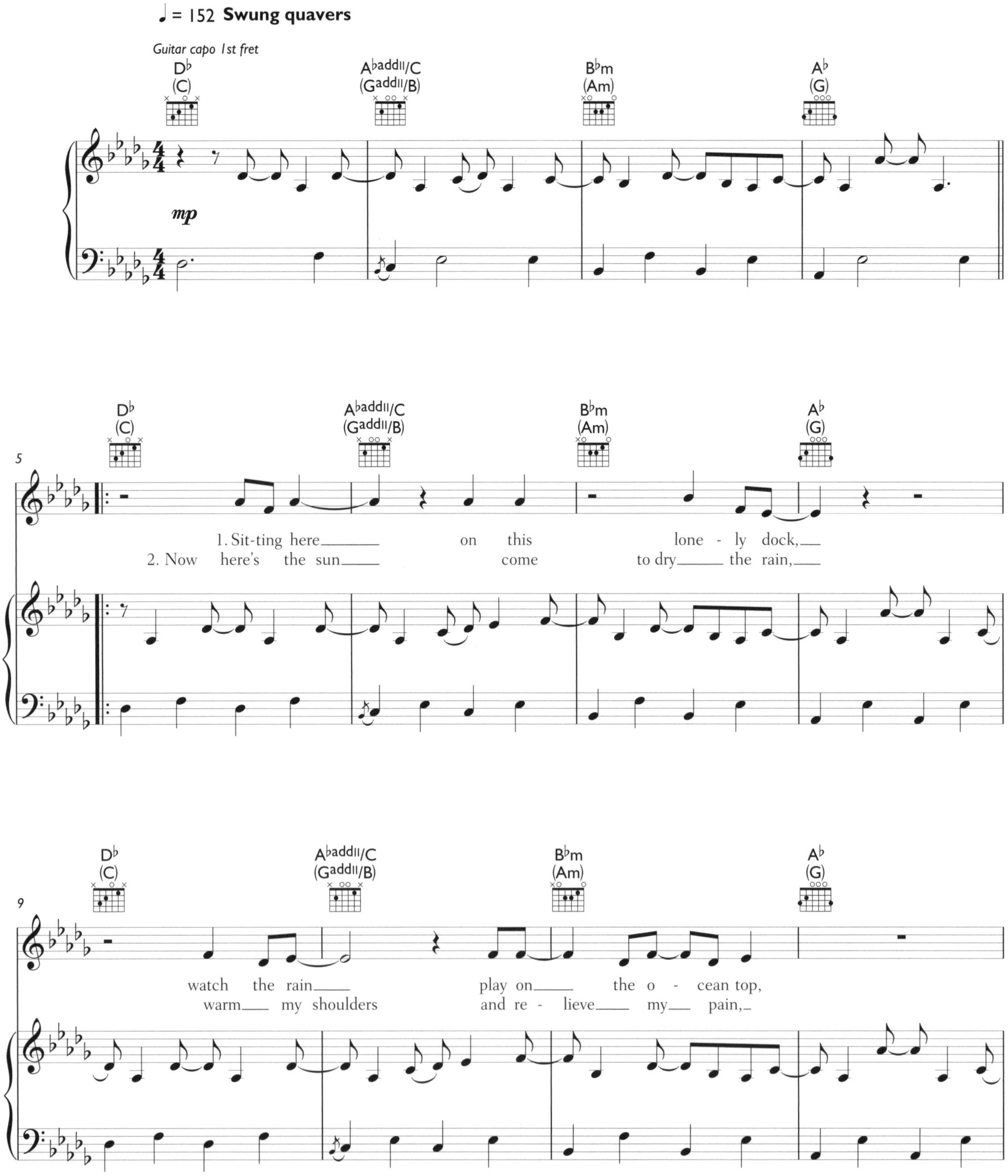
♩ = 152 Swung quavers
Guitar capo 1st fret
D♭ (C)
A♭add11/C (Gadd11/B)
B♭m (Am)
A♭ (G)
mp
5
1. Sit-ting here on this lone - ly dock,
2. Now here's the sun come to dry the rain,
9
watch the rain play on the o - cean top,
warm my shoulders and re - lieve my pain,

D♭ (C)
A♭add11/C (Gadd11/B)
B♭m (Am)
A♭ (G)
13
all the things I feel I need to say,
you're the one thing that I'm miss - ing here,
17
I can't ex - plain in a - ny o - ther way.
with you be - side me I no long - er fear.
I need to be bold,
G♭sus2 (Fsus2)
D♭ (C)
A♭/C (G/B)
21
need to jump in the cold wat - er, need to grow old - er with a girl like you, fi - nal - ly see
mf
25
you are na - tural - ly the one to make it so ea - sy when you show me the truth, yeah,

G♭sus2 (Fsus2)
A♭ (G)
D♭ (C)
A♭/C (G/B)
29
I'd ra - ther be with
B♭m (Am)
G♭sus2 (Fsus2)
A♭ (G)
32
you, say you want the same thing
1.
D♭ (C)
A♭add11/C (Gadd11/B)
B♭m (Am)
A♭ (G)
35
too.
2.
D♭ (C)
G♭sus2 (Fsus2)
B♭m (Am)
39
too. I could have saved

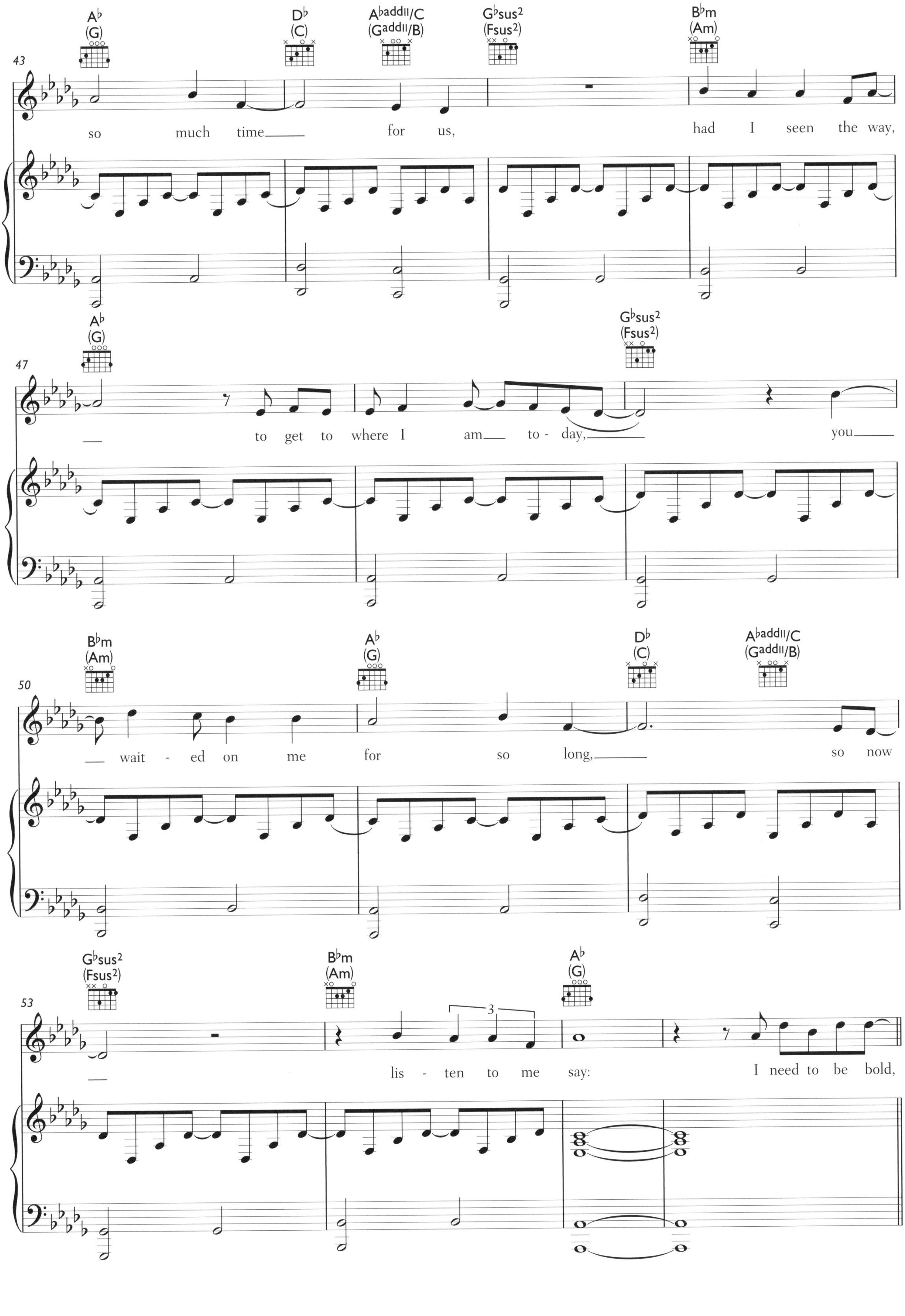

A♭ (G)
D♭ (C)
A♭addII/C (GaddII/B)
G♭sus2 (Fsus2)
B♭m (Am)
43
so much time for us, had I seen the way,
47
to get to where I am to-day, you
50
wait-ed on me for so long, so now
53
lis-ten to me say: I need to be bold,

G♭sus2 (Fsus2)
A♭ (G)
D♭ (C)
A♭/C (G/B)
57
— need to jump in the cold — wat - er, need to grow old - er with a girl like you,
B♭m (Am)
G♭sus2 (Fsus2)
A♭ (G)
60
— fi - nal - ly see — you are na - tural - ly the one to make it so ea -
B♭m (Am)
A♭ (G)
G♭sus2 (Fsus2)
63
- sy when you show me the truth, — yeah, —
A♭ (G)
D♭ (C)
A♭/C (G/B)
B♭m (Am)
66
3
I'd ra - ther be — with you, —

G♭sus2
(Fsus2)
A♭
(G)
D♭
(C)
69
say you want the same thing too,
D♭sus2
(Csus2)
B♭add9
Badd9
A♭
(G)
72
say you feel
D♭
(C)
A♭11
(G11)
D♭
(C)
75
the way I do.

LAST REQUEST

Words and Music by Paolo Giovanni Nutini, Jim Duguid, Matt Benbrook, Annunzio Paolo Mantovani, Stephen Foster and Nikolai Andrej Rimsky-Korsakoff

B♭ Dm Gm 3fr
10
-right? Ba-by let's get clo - ser to - night.
F Am/E Dm
13
Grant my last re-quest and just let me hold you, don't shrug your shoul-
Gm7 3fr B♭ C
15
3
-ders; lay down be-side me.
F Am/E Dm7
17
Sure I can ac - cept that we're go-ing no - where, but one last time let's

To Coda
Gm
B♭
C
F
go there, oh, lay down be - side me. 2. And I've found,
Am7
Cm
Gm
that I'm bound, to wan - der down that one - way road, oh.
F
Am7
And I re - al - ise all a - bout your lies, but I'm
Cm
Gm
no wis - er than the fool that I was be - fore. I just want you clo -

B♭
Dm
Gm
3fr
29
-ser, is that al - right? Ba - by let's get clo -
3
3
B♭
Dm
Gm
3fr
D.S. al Coda
31
-ser to - night.
Coda
B♭
Dm
Gm
3fr
Gm7
3fr
33
3
Ba - by, ba - by, ba - by, tell me how
B♭
Dm
Gm
3fr
35
can, how can this be wrong?

F
Am/E
Dm
37
Grant my last re-quest and just let me hold you, don't shrug your shoul-
Gm7
B♭
Cadd9
39
-ders; no, lay down be-side me. And sure,
F
F/E
Dm
41
I can ac-cept that we're go-ing no-where, but one last time let's go
Gm7
B♭
Cadd9
43
there; lay down be-side me.

F
F/E
Dm
45
3
Grant my last re - quest and just let me hold you, don't shrug your shoul -
Gm
3fr
B♭
Cadd9
47
- ders;
lay down de - cide me. And sure,
F
F/E
Dm7
49
I can ac - cept that we're go - ing no - where, but one last time let's go
Gm7
3fr
rall.
B♭
C
Fadd9
51
there;
lay down be - side...
Ped.

PATIENCE

Words and Music by Howard Donald, Jason Orange,
Gary Barlow, Mark Owen and John Shanks

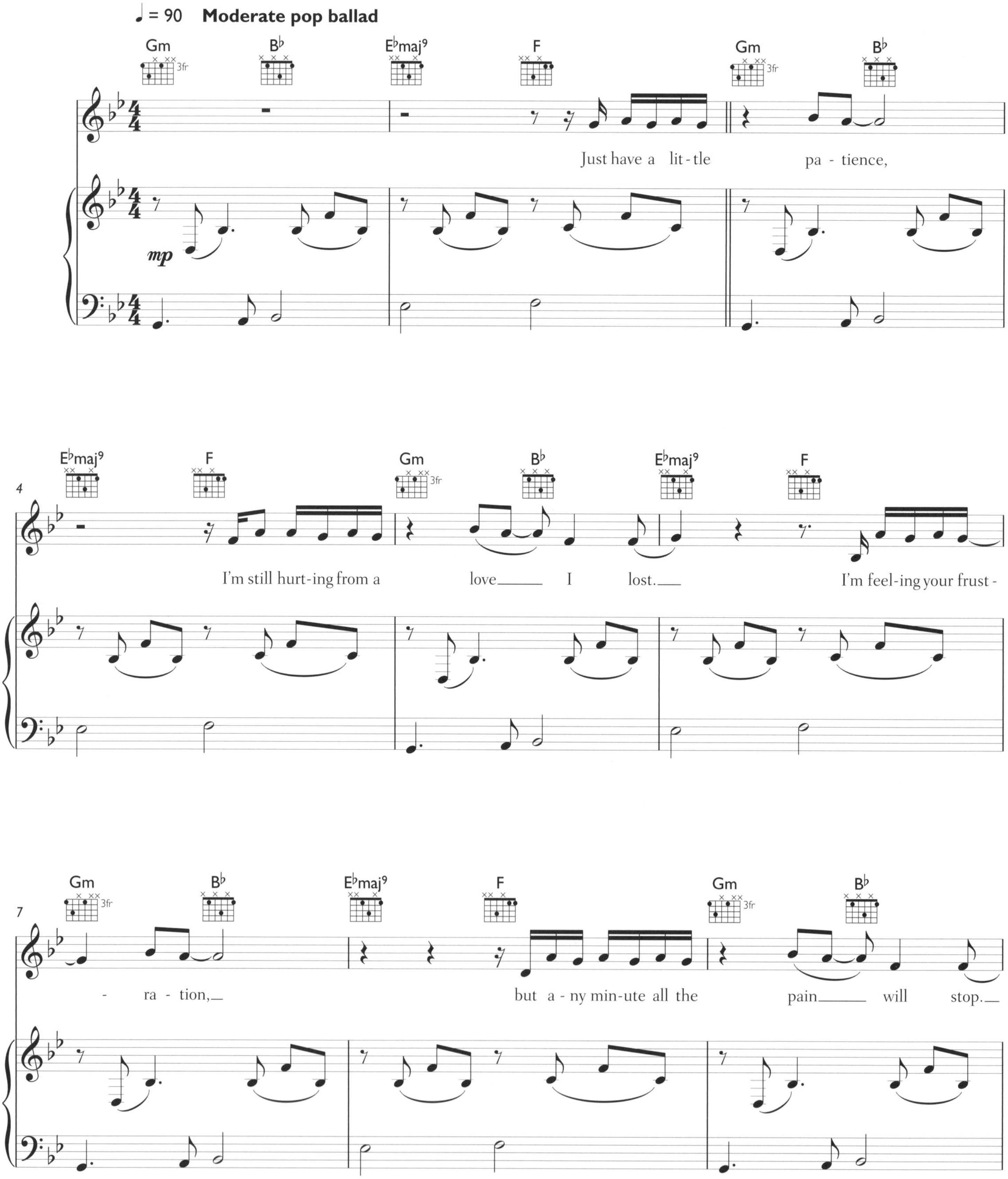
♩ = 90 Moderate pop ballad
Gm B♭ E♭maj9 F Gm B♭
Just have a lit-tle pa - tience,
mp
4
E♭maj9 F Gm B♭ E♭maj9 F
I'm still hurt-ing from a love I lost.
I'm feel-ing your frust -
7
Gm B♭ E♭maj9 F Gm B♭
- ra - tion,
but a - ny min-ute all the pain will stop.
3fr

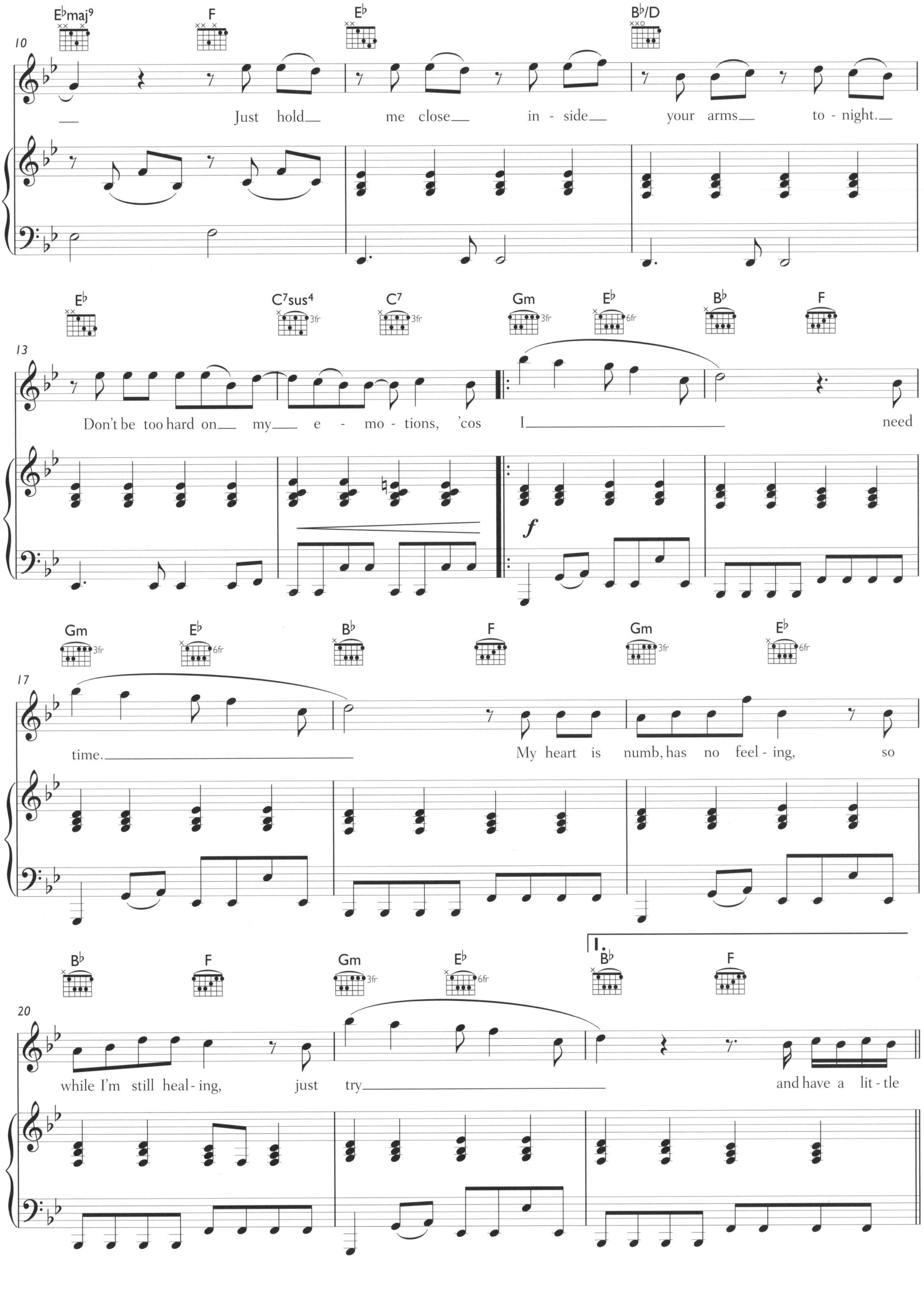
E♭maj9 F E♭ B♭/D
Just hold me close in - side your arms to - night.
E♭ C7sus4 C7 Gm E♭ B♭ F
Don't be too hard on my e - mo - tions, 'cos I need
f
Gm E♭ B♭ F Gm E♭
time. My heart is numb, has no feel - ing, so
B♭ F Gm E♭ 1. B♭ F
while I'm still heal - ing, just try and have a lit - tle

Gm B♭ E♭maj9 F Gm B♭
23
pa - tience. I real-ly wan-na start o - ver a - gain.
mp
E♭maj9 F Gm B♭ E♭maj9 F
26
I know you wan-na be my sal - va - tion, the one that I can
Gm B♭ E♭maj9 F E♭
29
al - ways de - pend. I'll try to be strong, be-lieve me
B♭/D E♭ C7sus4 C7
32
I'm try - ing to move on. It's com - pli - ca - ted but un - der - stand me, 'cause

2.
B♭ F9 A♭add9 E♭ B♭ B♭sus4 B♭
4fr
35
and have a lit - tle pa - tience, yeah. Have a lit - tle
A♭add9 E♭ B♭ Cm/B♭ E♭/D B♭ E♭ B♭/D
4fr
38
pa - tience, yeah. 'Cause the scars run so deep, it's been hard
Cm7 B♭ F/A B♭/A F7/C
3fr
41
but I have to be - lieve. Have a lit - tle
f
Gm B♭ E♭maj9 F Gm B♭
3fr 3fr
44
pa - tience. Have a lit - tle pa - tience.
mp

E♭maj9 F Gm E♭ B♭ F
47
Whoa, 'cos I, I just need
Gm E♭ B♭ F Gm E♭
50
time. My heart is numb, has no feel - ing so
B♭ F Gm E♭ B♭ F
53
while I'm still heal - ing, just try and have a lit - tle
Gm E♭ B♭ F
56
pa - tience, have a lit - tle

Gm
E♭
B♭
F
Gm
E♭
58
pa - tience.
My heart is numb, has no feel - ing,
so
B♭
F
Gm
E♭
61
while I'm still heal - ing,
just
try
B♭
F
Gm
63
and have a lit - tle
pa - tience.

I'M LIKE A BIRD

Words and Music by Nelly Furtado

B♭
F
E♭maj9
15
I won't ev - er change.
you don't know me that well.
And tho' my love is rare,
mf
F6
E♭maj9
F6
18
yeah, and tho' my love is true.
B♭
F6
Cm
3fr
21
I'm like a bird, I'll on-ly fly a - way,
I don't know where my soul is,
I don't know where my
E♭
B♭
F6
24
home is.
I'm like a bird, I'll on-ly fly a - way,
I don't know where my
(And, ba-by, all I need for you to know is:)

1.
Cm
3fr
27
soul is, I don't know_ where my
E♭
home is.
(and I need for you to know_ this:)
2. Your
2.
E♭
29
home is
(and ba - by, all I need for you to know is:)
E♭maj9
It's not that I wan - na say good - bye,
Gm7
3fr
31
6
it's just that ev - 'ry time you_ try to
E♭maj7
tell_ me,_ me,_ that you love_
F
33
— me, oh,_ oh,_
E♭maj9
each and ev - 'ry sin - gle day,_
GmII
I know I'm gon - na have_ to e - ven - tu - al - ly
3
3

E♭maj9
F
36
give you a - way, yeah, yeah, yeah, yeah.
And tho' my love is
E♭maj9
F6
F
E♭
39
rare, rare, rare, yeah, and tho' my love is true, yeah,
F
E♭
F6
F
42
hey, I'm just scared, yeah, yeah, that we may fall
E♭
F6
F
45
through-woo-woo-woo-woo-woo-woo-woo-woo, yeah, yeah, yeah, yeah.

B♭
F6
I'm like a bird,
I don't know where my
Cm
E♭
soul is, I don't know where my home is, (and ba - by, all I need for you is
B♭
F6
I'm like a bird, I'll on - ly fly a - way I don't know where my
know is:)
Cm
E♭
Repeat ad lib. to fade
soul is, I don't know where my home is (and ba - by, all I need for you to

REHAB

Words and Music by Amy Winehouse

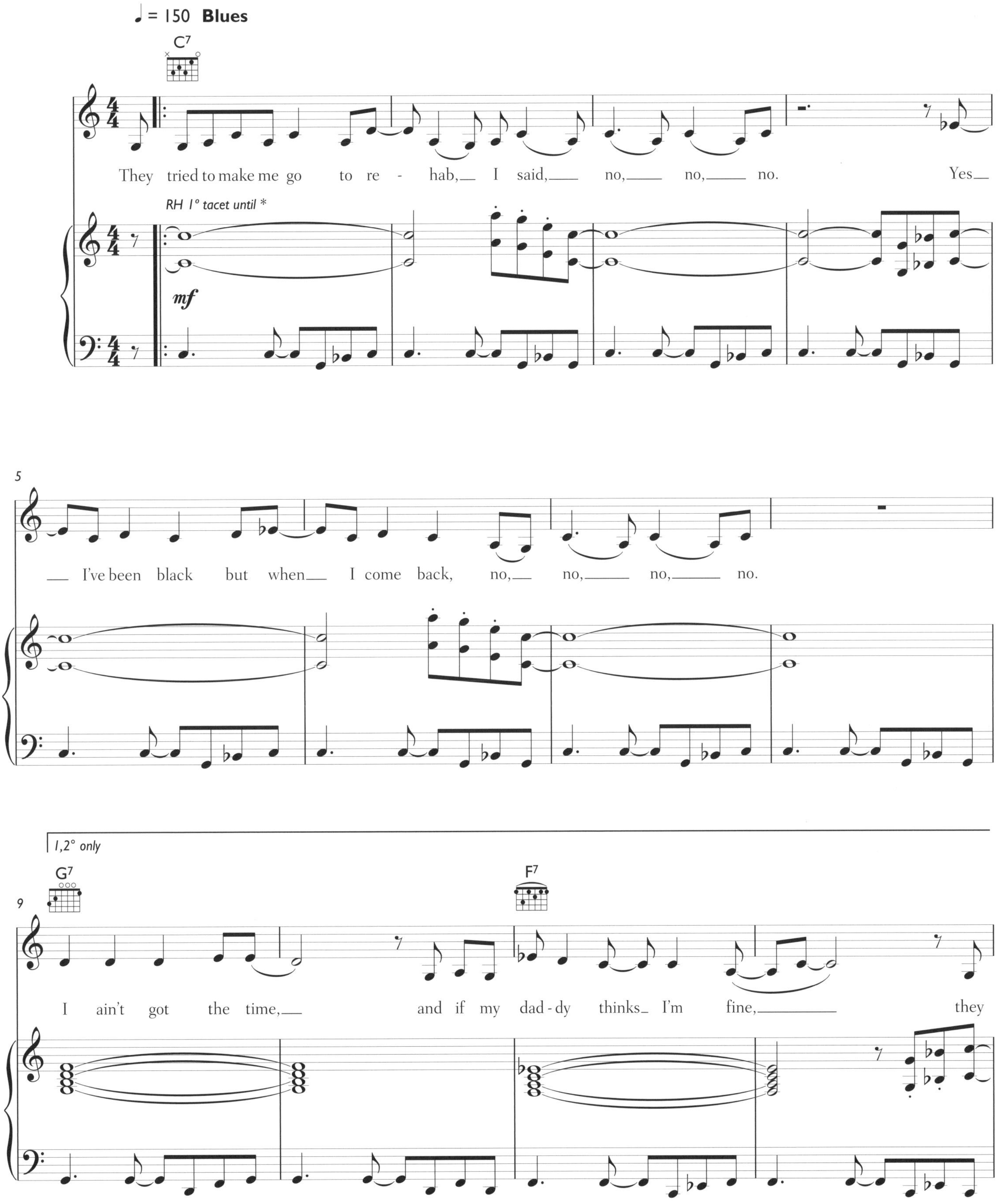

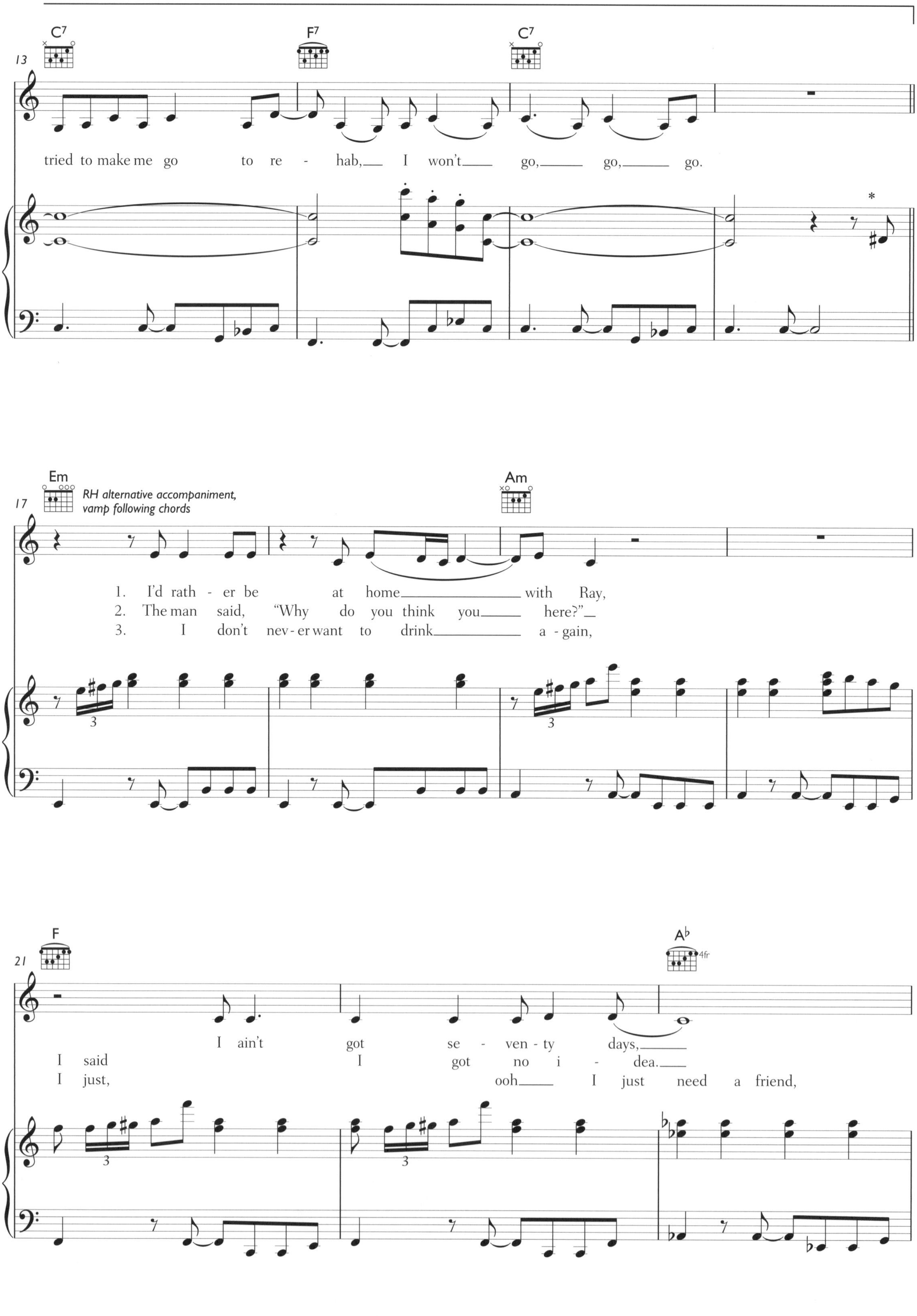
C7
F7
C7
13
tried to make me go to re - hab, I won't go, go, go.
*
Em
Am
17
RH alternative accompaniment, vamp following chords
1. I'd rath - er be at home with Ray,
2. The man said, "Why do you think you here?"
3. I don't nev - er want to drink a - gain,
3
F
A♭
4fr
21
I ain't got se - ven - ty days,
I said I got no i - dea.
I just, ooh I just need a friend,
3

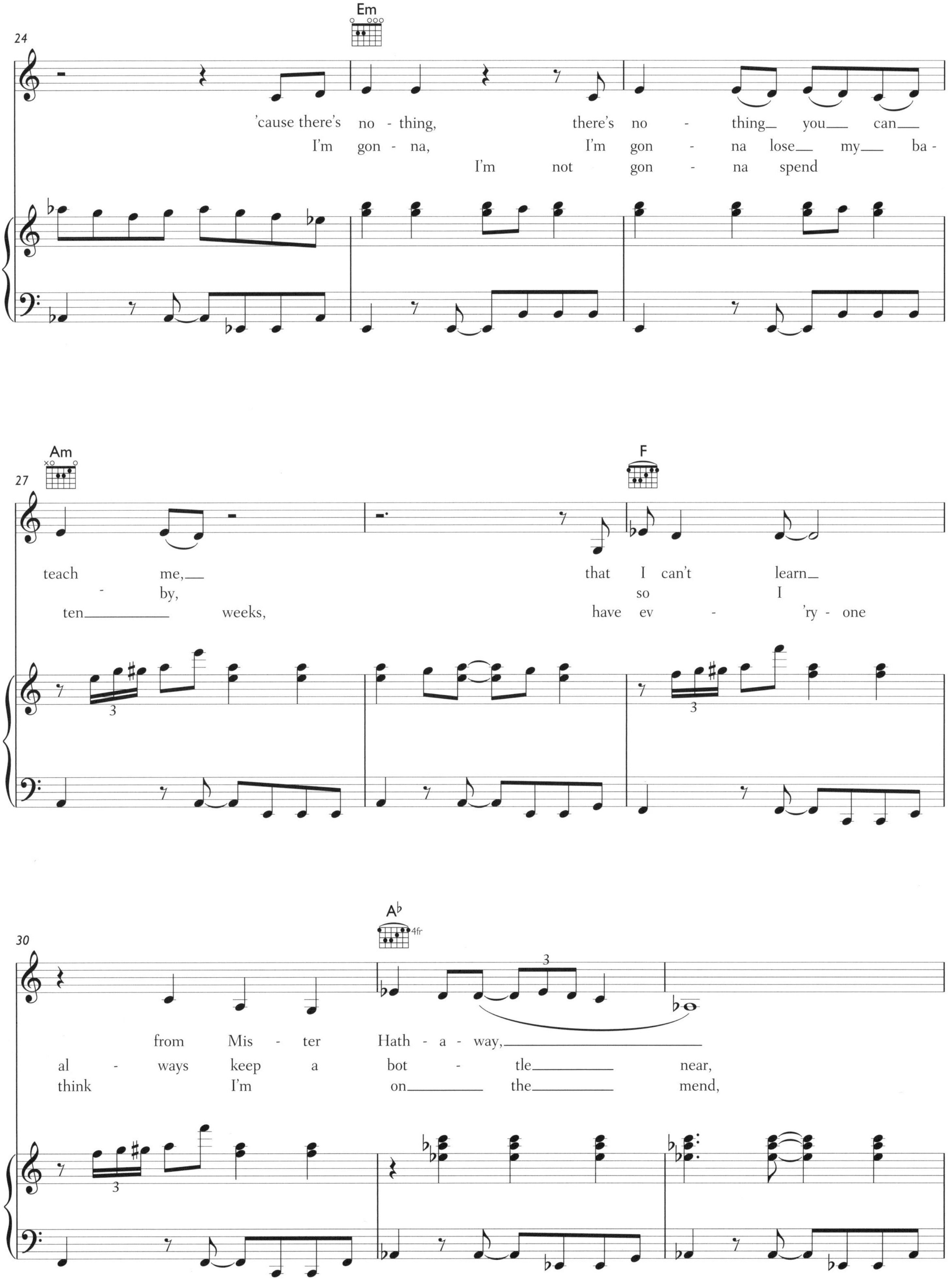
24
Em
'cause there's no - thing, there's no - thing you can
I'm gon - na, I'm gon - na lose my ba -
I'm not gon - na spend
27
Am
F
teach me, that I can't learn
- by, so I
ten weeks, have ev - 'ry - one
30
A♭
4fr
3
from Mis - ter Hath - a - way,
al - ways keep a bot - tle near,
think I'm on the mend,

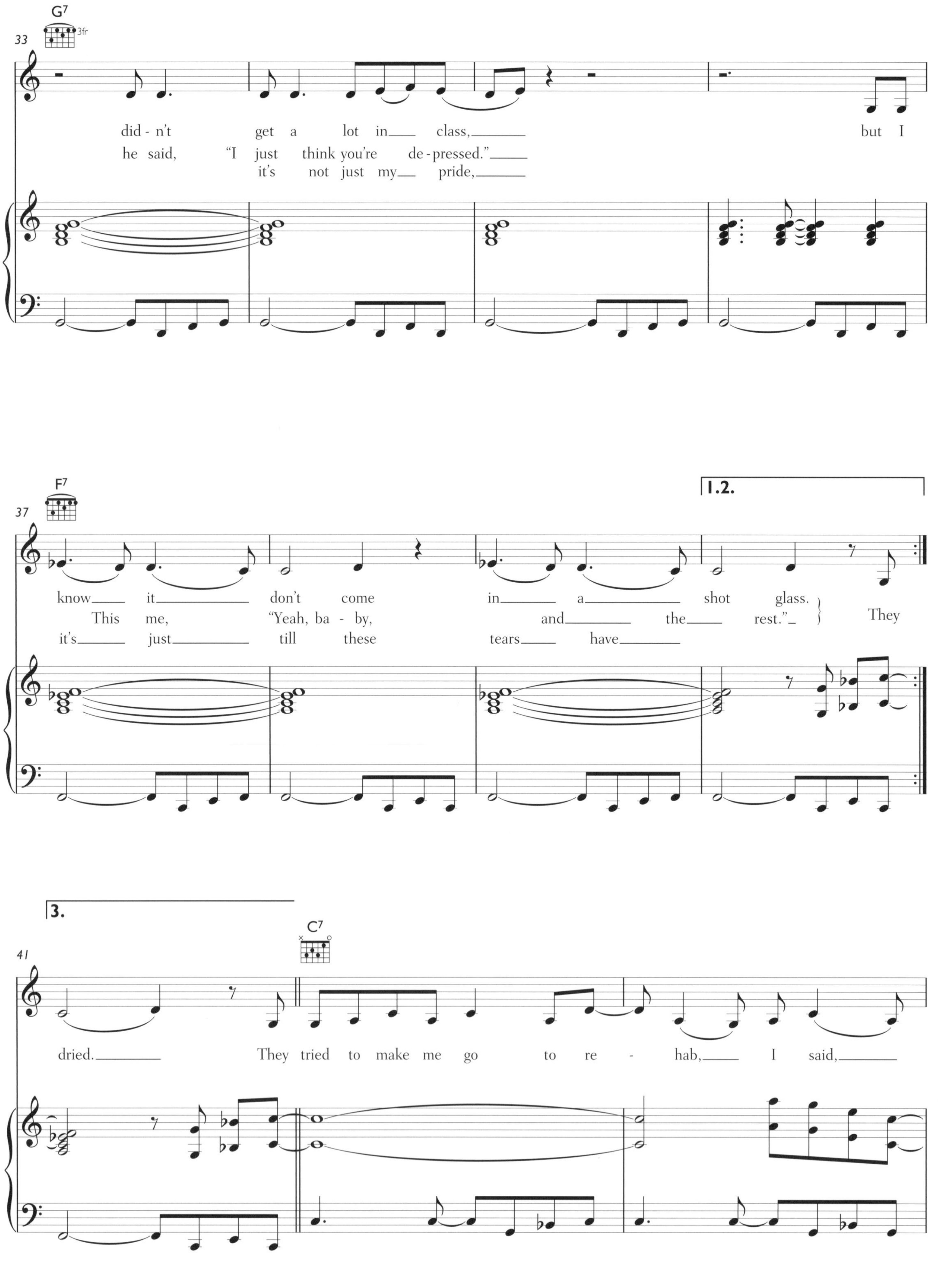
G7
3fr
33
did - n't get a lot in class, but I
he said, "I just think you're de - pressed."
it's not just my pride,
F7
37
1.2.
know it don't come in a shot glass.
This me, "Yeah, ba - by, and the rest."
They
it's just till these tears have
3.
41
C7
dried. They tried to make me go to re - hab, I said,

44
no, no, no. Yes I've been black but when
47
I come back, no, no, no, no.
G7
50
F7
I ain't got the time, and if my dad-dy thinks I'm fine, they
C7
54
F7
C7
N.C.
tried to make me go to re - hab, I won't go, go, go.

RUSSIAN ROULETTE

Words and Music by Charles Harmon and Shaffer Smith

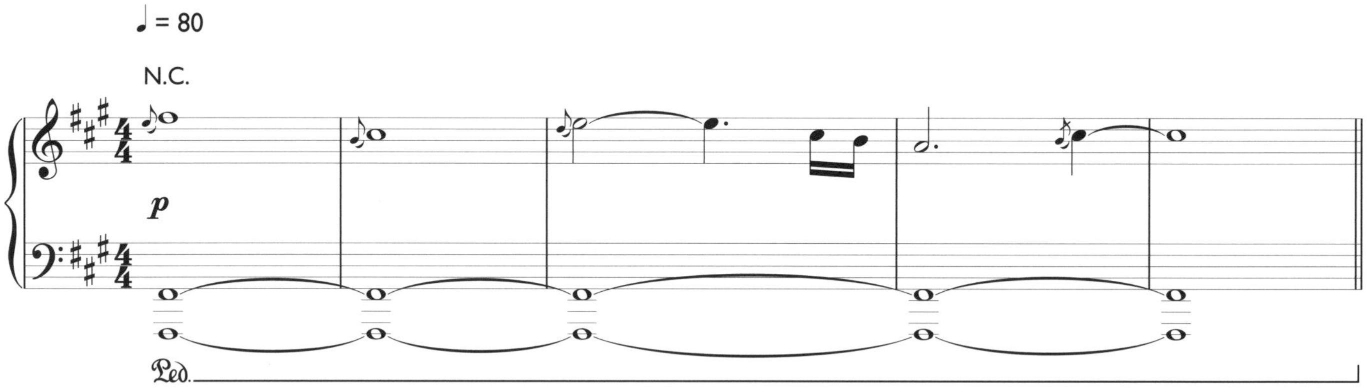

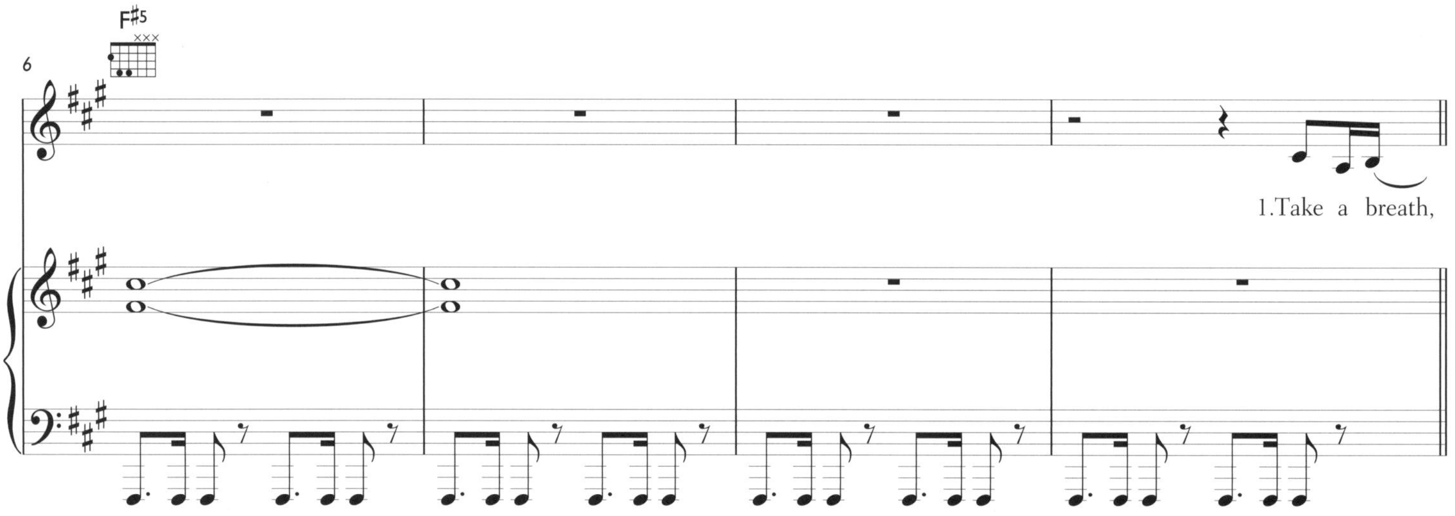

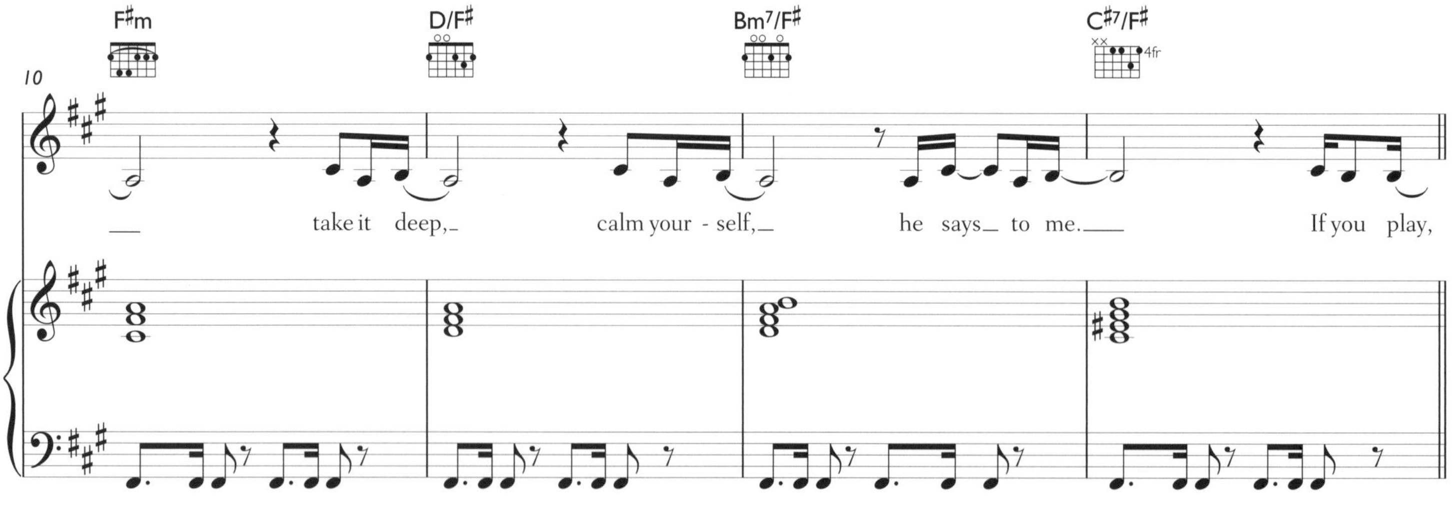

14
F♯m6
D/F♯
Bm7/F♯
you play for keeps, take the gun and count to three.
(2.) to your-self, he says, close your eyes some-times it helps.
17
C♯7/F♯
4fr
F♯m
D/F♯
I'm sweat-in' now, mov-in' slow, no time to think,
And then I give a scar-y thought that he's here
20
Bm7
C♯7
4fr
F♯m
D
my turn to go.
means he's ne-ver lost.
And you can see my heart beat-ing,
mf
24
E
Bm
F♯m
D
you can see it through my chest that I'm ter-ri-fied, but I'm not leav-ing, I

1.
2.
To Coda
E
Bm
C♯7
4fr
N.C.
know that I must pass this test, so just pull the trig-ger. 2. Say a prayer
so just pull the trig - ger. As my life flash-es be-fore my eyes I'm
D
A
f
Bm7
F♯m
F♯m/E
won-der-ing will I ev-er see an-o-ther sun-rise? So ma-ny won't get the
B/D♯
Esus4
C♯7/F
D. % al Coda
chance to say good-bye, but it's too late to think of the va-lue of my life. And you can see my heart
ff

Coda
Bm
F♯m
D
E
C♯7
4fr
N.C.
You can see my heart beat - ing, oh
you can see it through my chest that I'm ter - ri - fied but I'm not leav -
- ing no, no, I know that I must pass this test, so just pull the trig -
- ger.
gunshot

Fyfe Dangerfield

SHE'S ALWAYS A WOMAN

Words and Music by Billy Joel

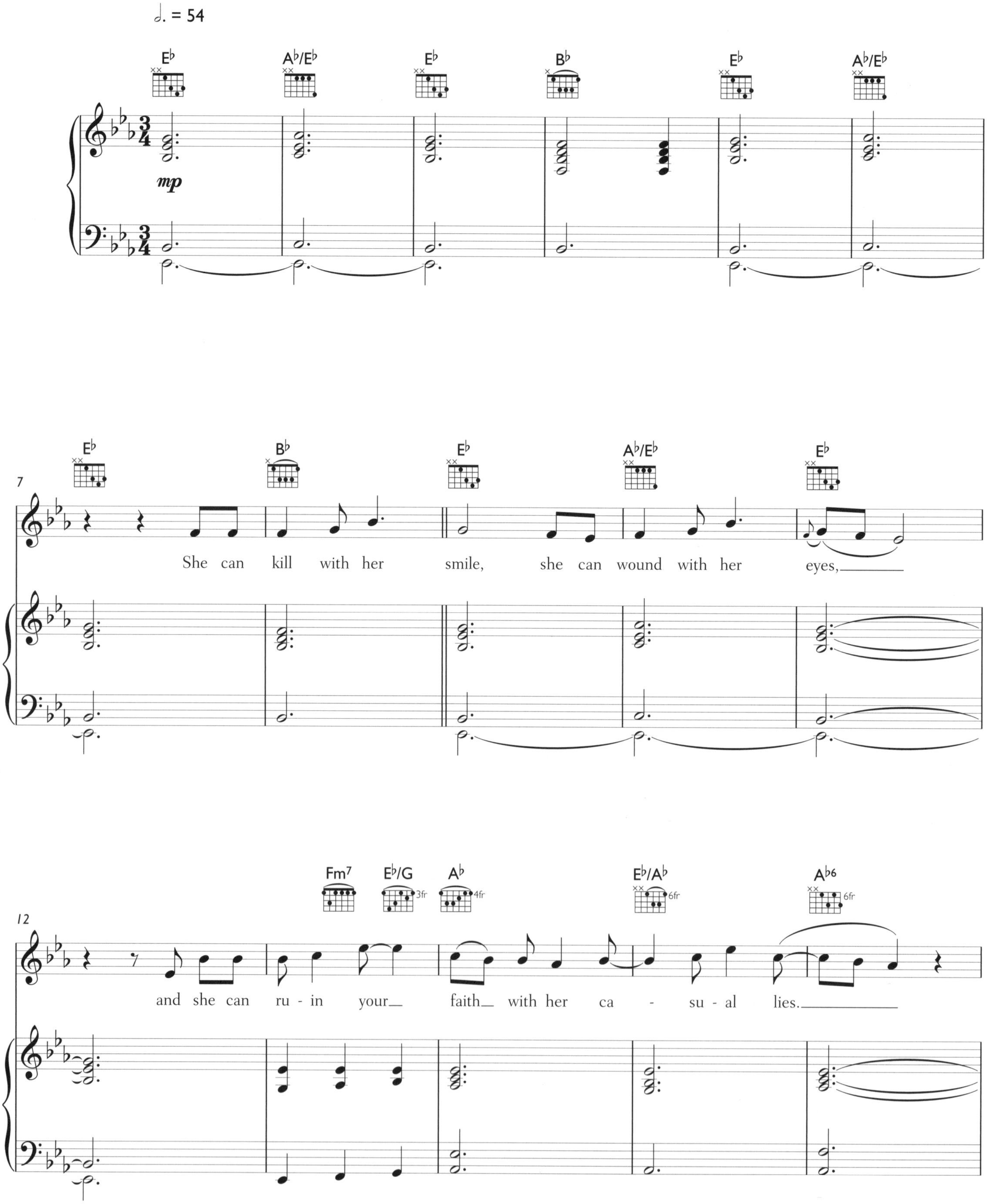
♩. = 54
E♭ A♭/E♭ E♭ B♭ E♭ A♭/E♭
mp
7
E♭ B♭ E♭ A♭/E♭ E♭
She can kill with her smile, she can wound with her eyes,
12
Fm7 E♭/G A♭ E♭/A♭ A♭6
3fr 4fr 6fr 6fr
and she can ru - in your faith with her ca - su - al lies.

A♭ B♭ E♭ B♭ G
6fr 6fr 6fr
17
And she on - ly re - veals what she wants you to see,
Cm Cm/B♭ Fm/A♭ Fm7/B♭
8fr 8fr 5fr 6fr
22
she hides like a child but she's al - ways a wo - man to
E♭ A♭/E♭ E♭ B♭
27
me. She can lead you to
E♭ A♭/B♭ E♭
31
love, she can take you or leave you. She can

Fm7 E♭/G A♭ E♭/A♭ A♭
35
ask for the truth_ but she'll nev - er be - lieve._
B♭ E♭ B♭ G
39
And she'll take what you'll give her_ as long as it's free.
Cm B♭6 Fm/A♭
44
Yes she steals like a thief but she's al - ways a
Fm7/B♭ E♭ A♭/B♭ E♭ E♭/D
48
wo - man_ to me.

Cm
Cm/B♭
Am7♭5
8fr
5fr
F
3fr
B♭
53
Oh, she takes care of her - self,
mf
B♭/A
Gm
E♭
A♭
4fr
A♭/G
58
she can wait if she wants,
Fm7
B♭
E♭
A♭/B♭
E♭
63
she's a - head of her time.
B♭6
E♭m
E♭m/D♭
A♭/C
68
Oh, and she

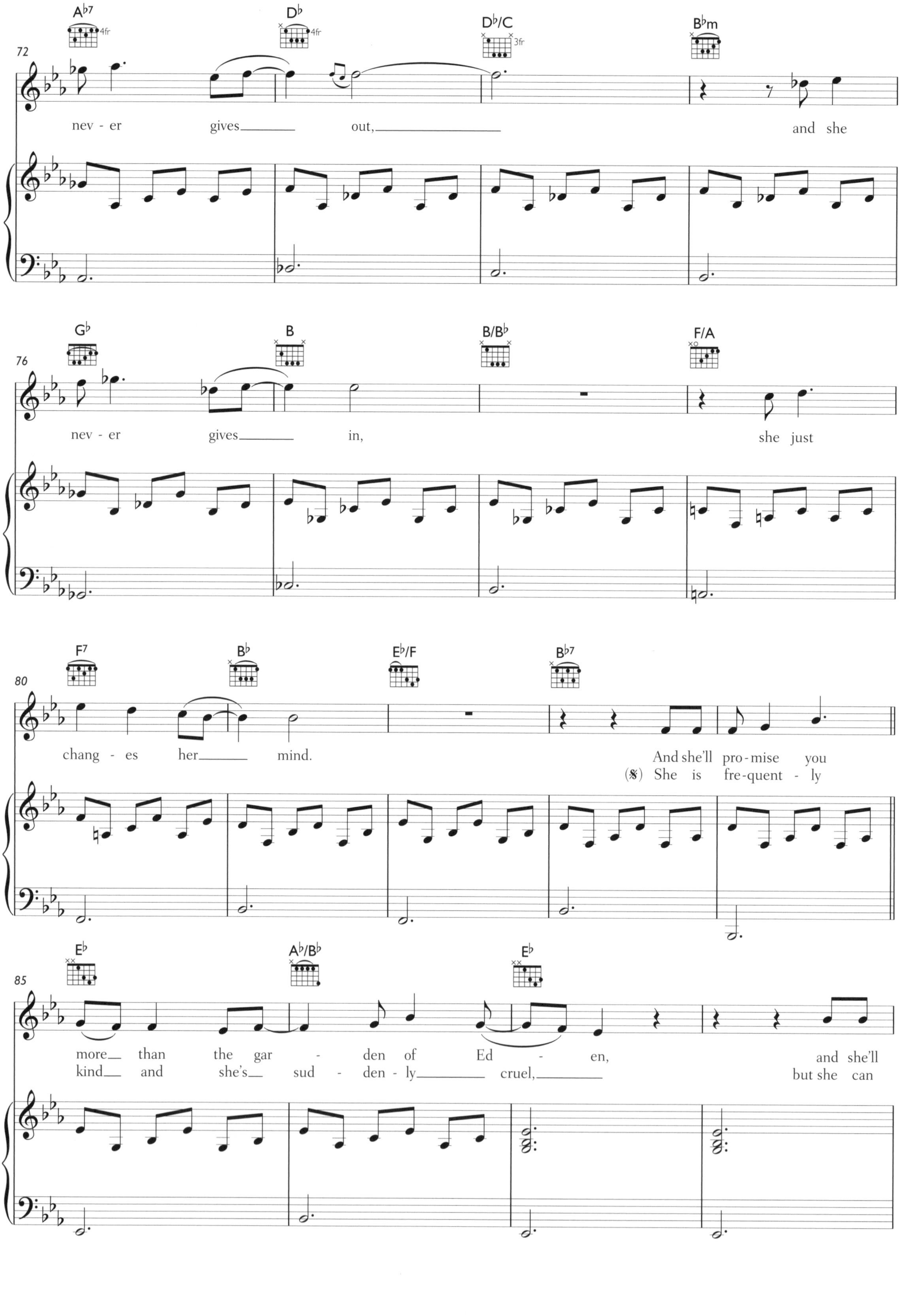
A♭7
4fr
D♭
4fr
D♭/C
3fr
B♭m
72
never gives out, and she
G♭
B
B/B♭
F/A
76
never gives in, she just
F7
B♭
E♭/F
B♭7
80
changes her mind.
And she'll promise you
(𝄋) She is frequently
E♭
A♭/B♭
E♭
85
more than the garden of Eden, and she'll
kind and she's suddenly cruel, but she can

Fm7 E♭/G A♭ E♭6 A♭6
89
care - less - ly cut you and laugh while you're bleed - ing.
do as she pleas - es she's no - bo - dy's fool.
A♭ B♭ E♭ B♭
93
But she'll bring out the best and the worst you can
And she can't be con - vic - ted, she's earned her de -
G To Coda Cm B♭6
97
be, blame it all on your - self 'cause she's al -
- gree. and the
A♭ A♭/B♭ E♭ A♭/B♭
101
- ways a wo - man to me.

E♭
B♭
E♭
B♭
105
Mmm,
G
Cm
Cm/B♭
Fm/A♭
109
mmm...
Fm7/B♭
E♭
114
D.𝄋 al Coda 𝄌
𝄌 Coda
Cm
B♭6
A♭
E♭/G
99
most she will do is throw sha-dows at you, but she's

Fm7
Ab/Bb
Eb
Ab/Bb
Eb
103
al- ways a wo- man_ to me.
Mmm,_
Bb
Eb
Bb
G
108
Cm
8fr
Cm/Bb
8fr
Fm/Ab
4fr
112
mmm...
rall.
Ab/Bb
Eb
Ab/Bb
Eb
116

SUPERSTAR

Words and Music by Mich Hansen, Joseph Belmaati and Mikkel Sigvardt

♩= 112 Funky
N.C.(E♭)
mf
5
(D♭)
(E♭)
E♭m
6fr
9
1. Peo - ple al - ways talk a - bout (ey oh, ey oh, ey oh.) all the things they're al a - bout.
2. Ba - by take a look a - round, (ey oh, ey oh, ey oh.) ev - 'ry - bo - dy's get - ting down.
12
D♭
4fr
(ey oh, ey oh, ey oh.) Write it on a piece of pap - er,
(ey oh, ey oh, ey oh.) Deal with all the prob - lems lat - er,

E♭m
15
got a feel - ing I'll see you lat - er.
bad boys on their best be - ha - viour.
There's some - thing
There's some - thing
E♭m
17
'bout this,
'bout you
let's keep it mov - ing,
and if it's good let's just get some - thing
20
cook - ing,
'cause I real - ly wan - na rock with
D♭
you.
I'm
22
feel - ing some con - nec - tion to the things you
E♭m
do.
N.C.
(You do, you do.)
I don't know

E♭m
25
what it is that makes me feel like this, I don't know who you are, but you must
D♭
28
be some kind of sup - er - star, 'cos you got all eyes on you no mat - ter
E♭m
To Coda
E♭m
31
where you are. (You just make me wan - na play.) I like the way you're mov - ing,
34
(ey oh, ey oh, ey oh.) I just get in - to the grove and then (you just make me wan - na play.)

37
D♭ 4fr
E♭m 6fr
If you just put pen to pa - per, (ey oh, ey oh, ey oh.) Got that feel-ing I'll see you lat - er.
40
N.C. (E♭)
Make your move, can we get a lit - tle clos - er?
(ey oh, ey oh, ey oh.)
43
(D♭)
You rock it just like you're sup-posed to. Hey,
46
(E♭)
D.𝄋 al Coda
(ad lib. vocal)
boy I ain't got no- thing more to say 'cos you just make me wan - na

Coda
E♭m
I don't know what it is that makes me
(you just make me wan - na play.)
feel like this, I don't know who you are, but you must be some kind of
D♭
E♭m
sup - er - star, 'cos you got all eyes on you no mat - ter where you are.
1.
2.
I don't know (You just make me wan - na play.)
(you just make me wan - na)

VALERIE

Words and Music by Dave McCabe, Sean Payne,
Abigail Harding, Boyan Chowdhury and Russell Pritchard

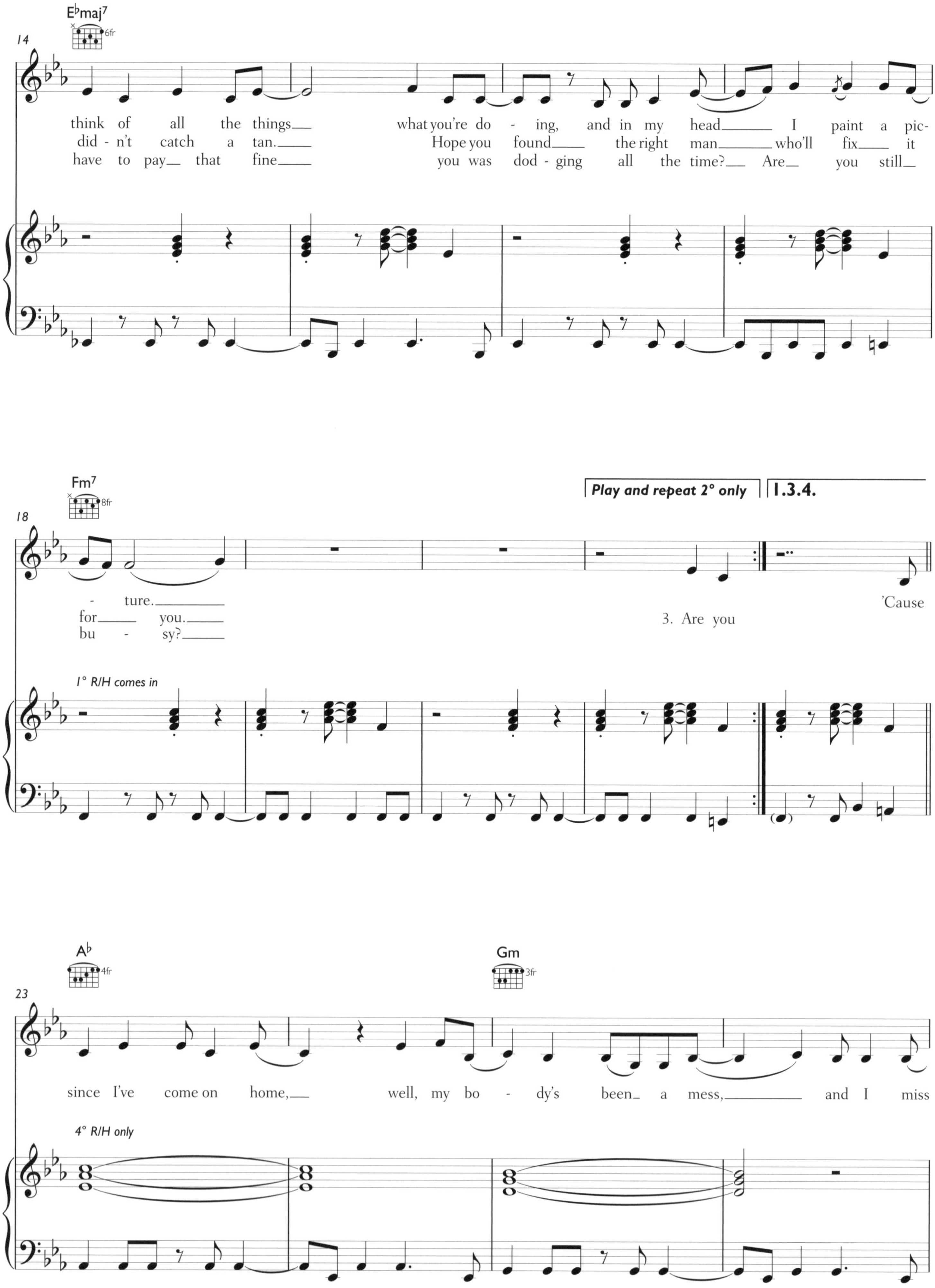
E♭maj7
6fr
14
think of all the things what you're do - ing, and in my head I paint a pic-
did - n't catch a tan. Hope you found the right man who'll fix it
have to pay that fine you was dod - ging all the time? Are you still
Fm7
8fr
18
Play and repeat 2° only
1.3.4.
- ture.
for you.
bu - sy?
3. Are you
'Cause
1° R/H comes in
A♭
4fr
Gm
3fr
23
since I've come on home, well, my bo - dy's been a mess, and I miss
4° R/H only

A♭
4fr
Gm
3fr
27
your gin - ger hair,
and the way you like to dress.
A♭
4fr
Gm
3fr
31
Ah won't you come on o - ver?
Stop ma - king a fool out of me.
4° L/H comes in
B♭
6fr
B♭7
6fr
35
Why don't you come on o - ver Va -
E♭maj7
6fr
39
- - le - rie?
Va - le - rie,

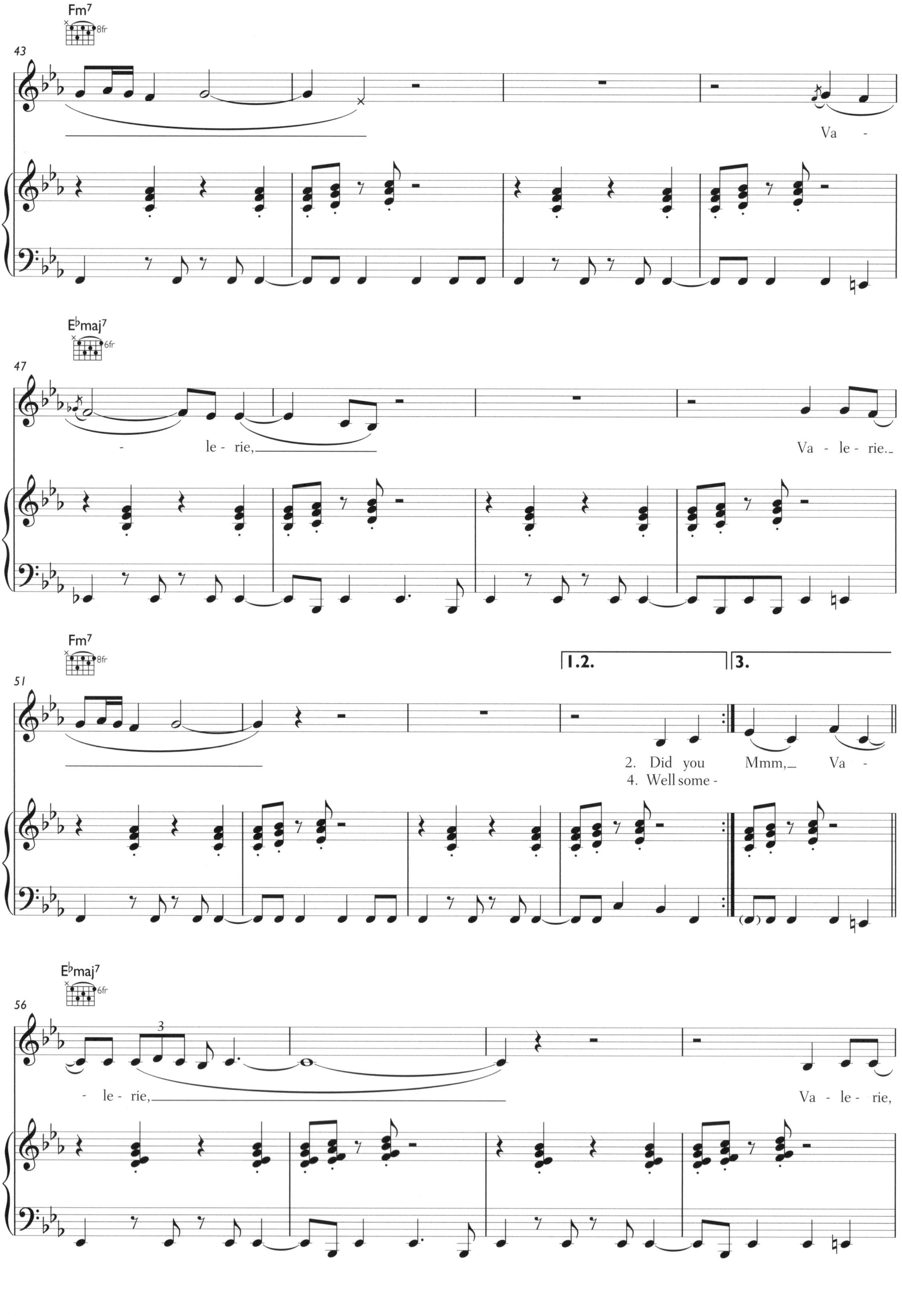
Fm7
8fr
43
Va -
E♭maj7
6fr
47
- le - rie,
Va - le - rie.
Fm7
8fr
51
1.2.
3.
2. Did you
4. Well some -
Mmm,
Va -
E♭maj7
6fr
56
3
- le - rie,
Va - le - rie,

Fm7
8fr
60
ah, Va - le -
E♭maj7
6fr
64
- rie.
Va - le -
Fm7
8fr
68
- rie.
Why don't you come on o - ver Va - le - rie?
E♭maj7
6fr

Toni Braxton

UNBREAK MY HEART

Words and Music by Diane Warren

Bm Em7 A
9
need your arms to hold me now, nights are so un - kind,
can't for - get the day you left, time is so un - kind,
Bm Em7 A
11
bring back those nights when I held you be - side me.
and life is so cruel with-out you here be - side me.
Un - break my heart
Dm Gm7 3fr C A7
13
say you love me a - gain.
Un - do this hurt
Dm Gm7 3fr C A7
15
you caused when you walked out the door and walked out of my life.
Un - cry these tears

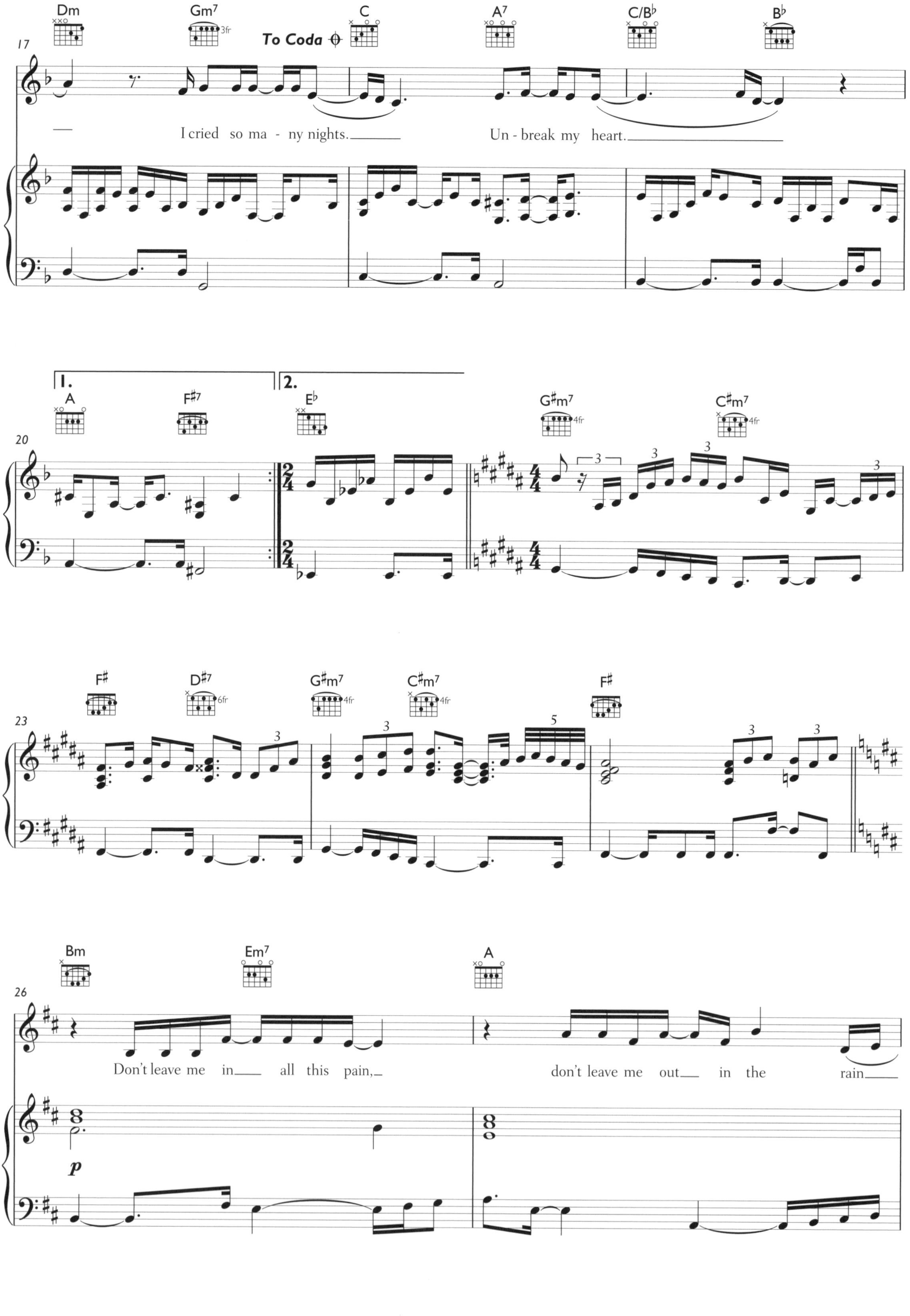
Dm
Gm7
3fr
To Coda
C
A7
C/B♭
B♭
I cried so ma - ny nights.
Un - break my heart.
1.
2.
A
F♯7
E♭
G♯m7
4fr
C♯m7
4fr
F♯
D♯7
6fr
G♯m7
4fr
C♯m7
4fr
F♯
Bm
Em7
A
Don't leave me in all this pain,
don't leave me out in the rain
p

Bm
Em7
A
D.𝄋 al Coda
bring back those nights when I held you be-side me. Un-break my heart.
f
Coda
C
A7
Dm
Gm7
3fr
Un-break my, un-break my heart, oh ba-by,
come back and say you love me. Un-break my heart, sweet darl-ing,
with-out you I just can't go on.
Repeat ad lib. to fade

WARWICK AVENUE

Words and Music by Duffy, Jimmy Hogarth and Eg White

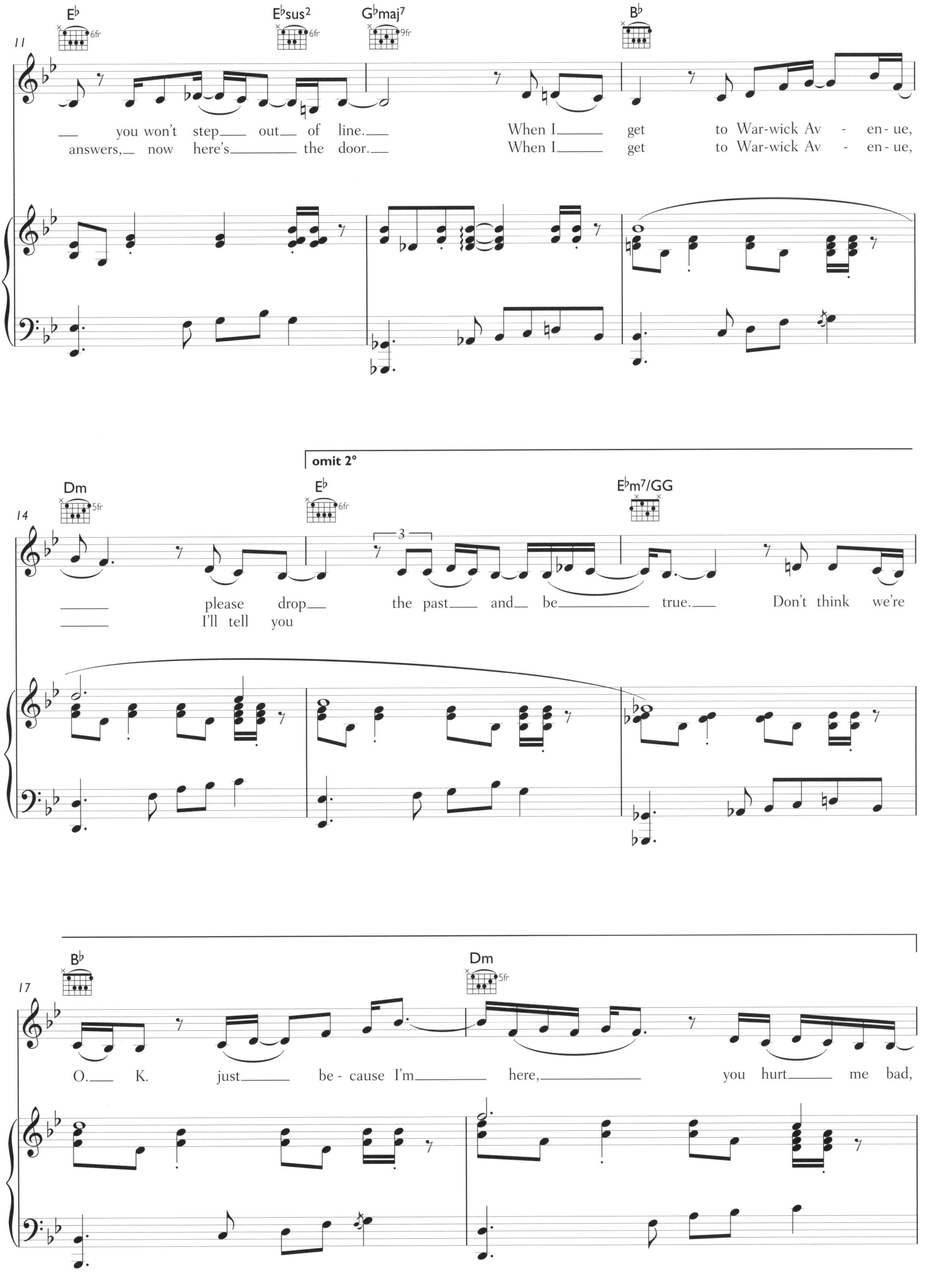
E♭
E♭sus2
G♭maj7
B♭
11
you won't step out of line.
answers, now here's the door.
When I get to War-wick Av - en - ue,
When I get to War-wick Av - en - ue,
omit 2°
Dm
E♭
E♭m7/GG
14
please drop the past and be true.
I'll tell you
Don't think we're
B♭
Dm
17
O. K. just be - cause I'm here,
you hurt me bad,

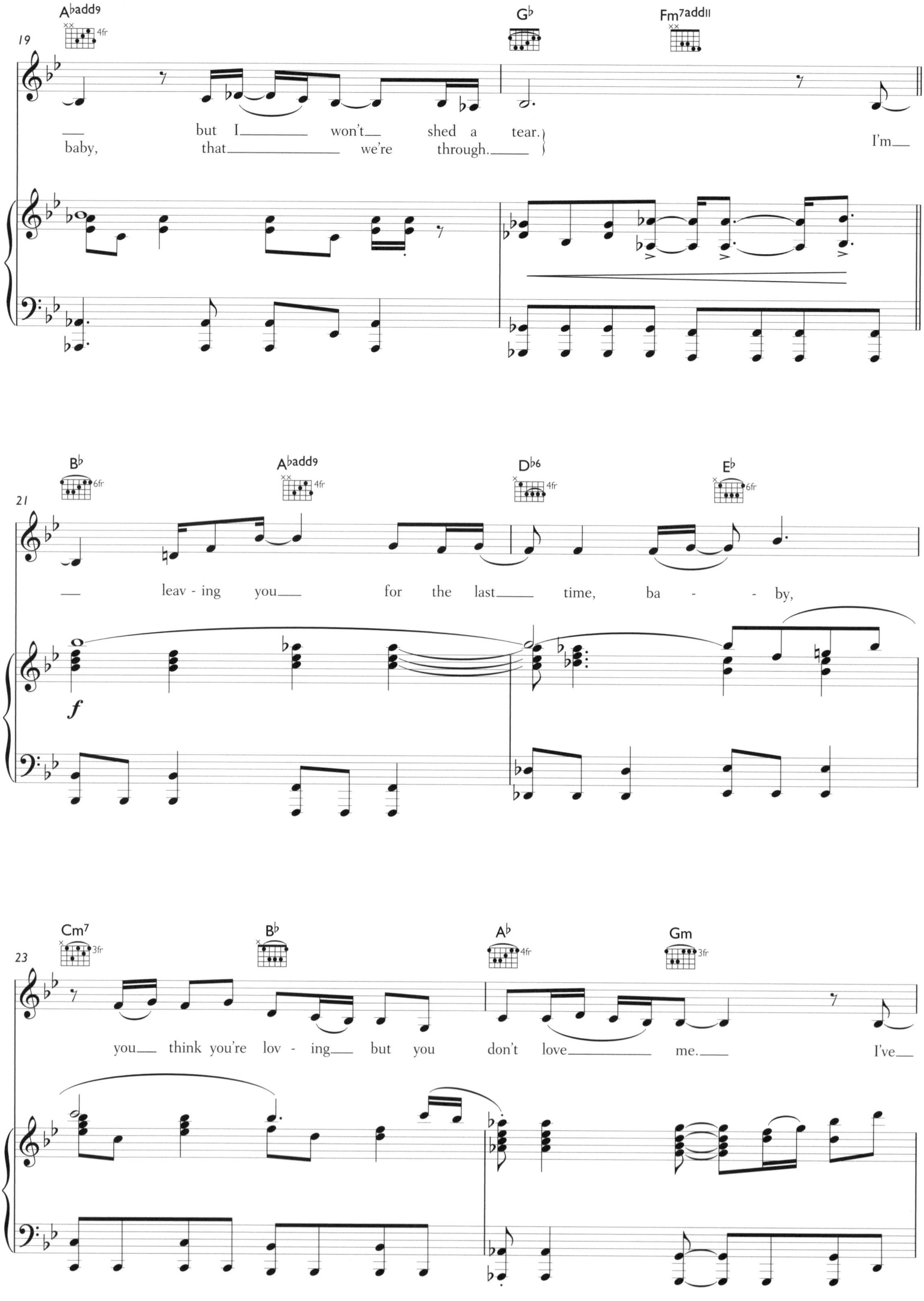
A♭add9
4fr
19
G♭
Fm7add11
— but I won't shed a tear.
baby, that we're through.
I'm
B♭
6fr
A♭add9
4fr
D♭6
4fr
E♭
6fr
21
— leav - ing you for the last time, ba - - by,
f
Cm7
3fr
B♭
A♭
4fr
Gm
3fr
23
you think you're lov - ing but you don't love me.
I've

Cm
3fr
Gm7add11
5fr
Fm7add11
25
been con - fused out of my mind late - ly,
1.
E♭
6fr
N.C.
Dm7
B♭/C
Gm7
Cm7
3fr
B♭
27
you think you're lov - ing but I want to be free, ba - by you've hurt me.
mp
Dm
5fr
E♭
6fr
E♭sus2
6fr
G♭maj7
9fr
G♭maj9
9fr
30
2. When I

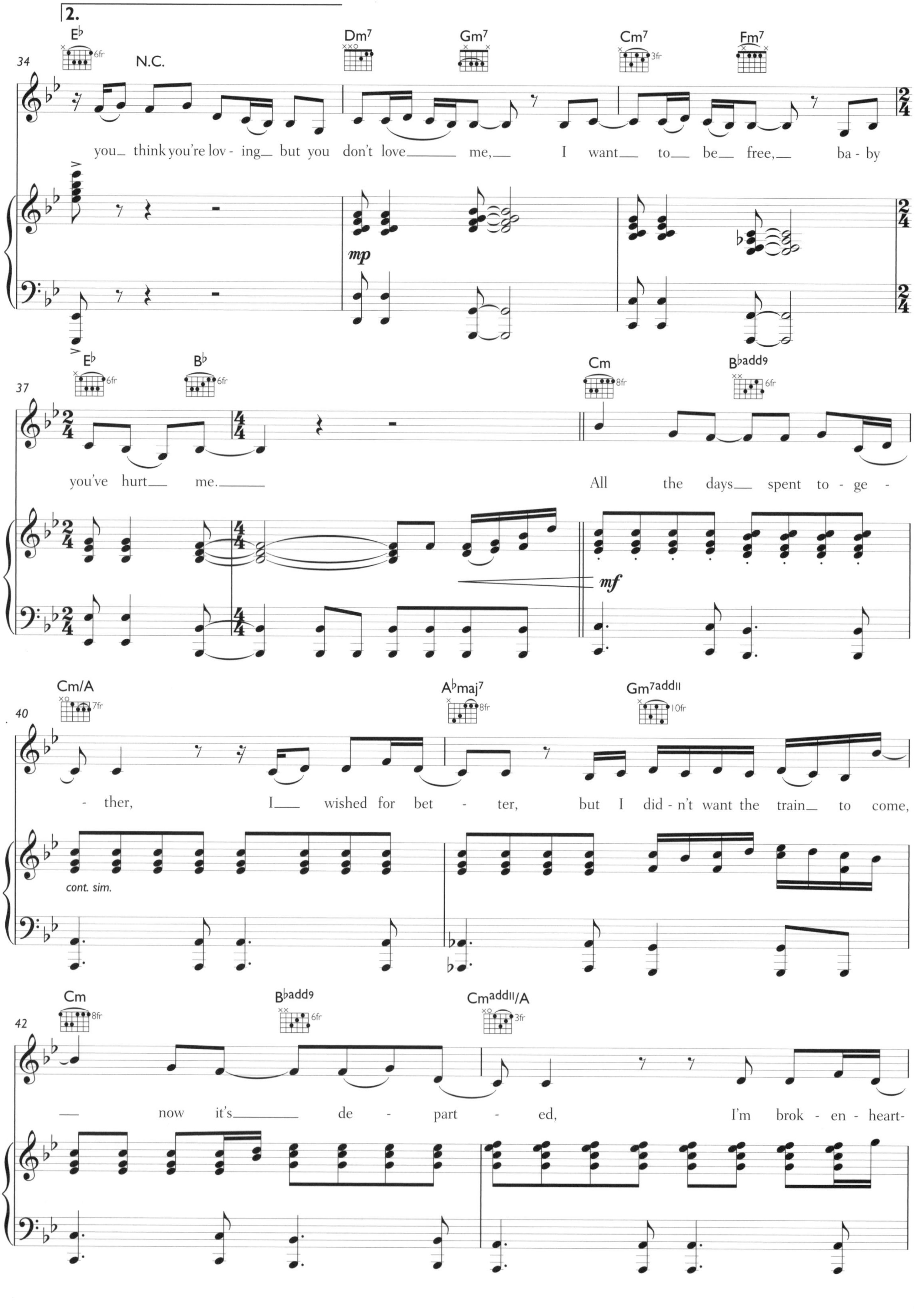
2.
34
E♭ N.C. Dm7 Gm7 Cm7 Fm7
you think you're lov - ing but you don't love me, I want to be free, ba - by
mp
37
E♭ B♭ Cm B♭add9
you've hurt me. All the days spent to - ge -
mf
40
Cm/A A♭maj7 Gm7add11
- ther, I wished for bet - ter, but I did - n't want the train to come,
cont. sim.
42
Cm B♭add9 Cmadd11/A
now it's de - part - ed, I'm brok - en - heart-

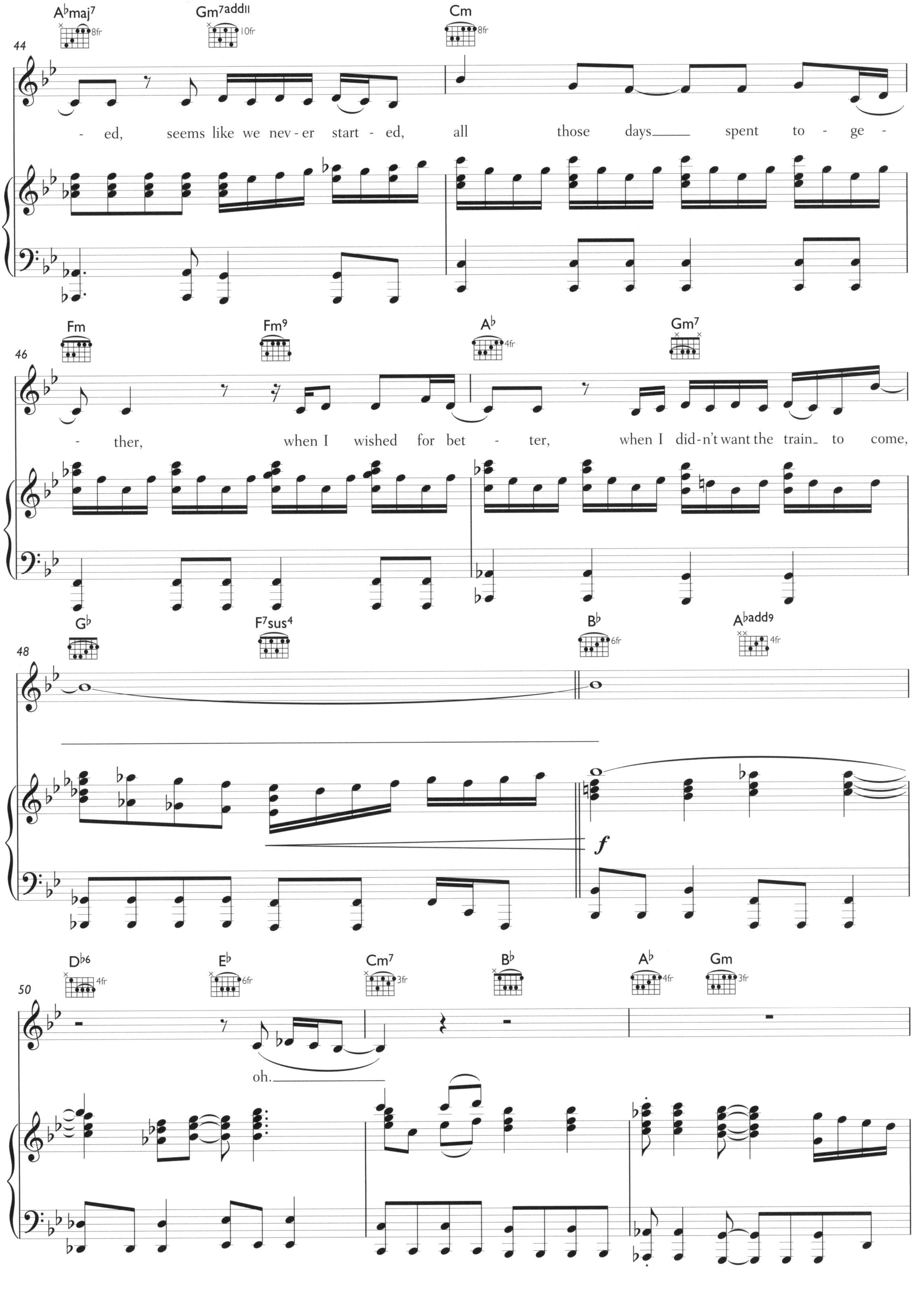
A♭maj7 Gm7add11 Cm
44
- ed, seems like we nev-er start - ed, all those days spent to - ge -
Fm Fm9 A♭ Gm7
46
- ther, when I wished for bet - ter, when I did-n't want the train to come,
G♭ F7sus4 B♭ A♭add9
48
f
D♭6 E♭ Cm7 B♭ A♭ Gm
50
oh.

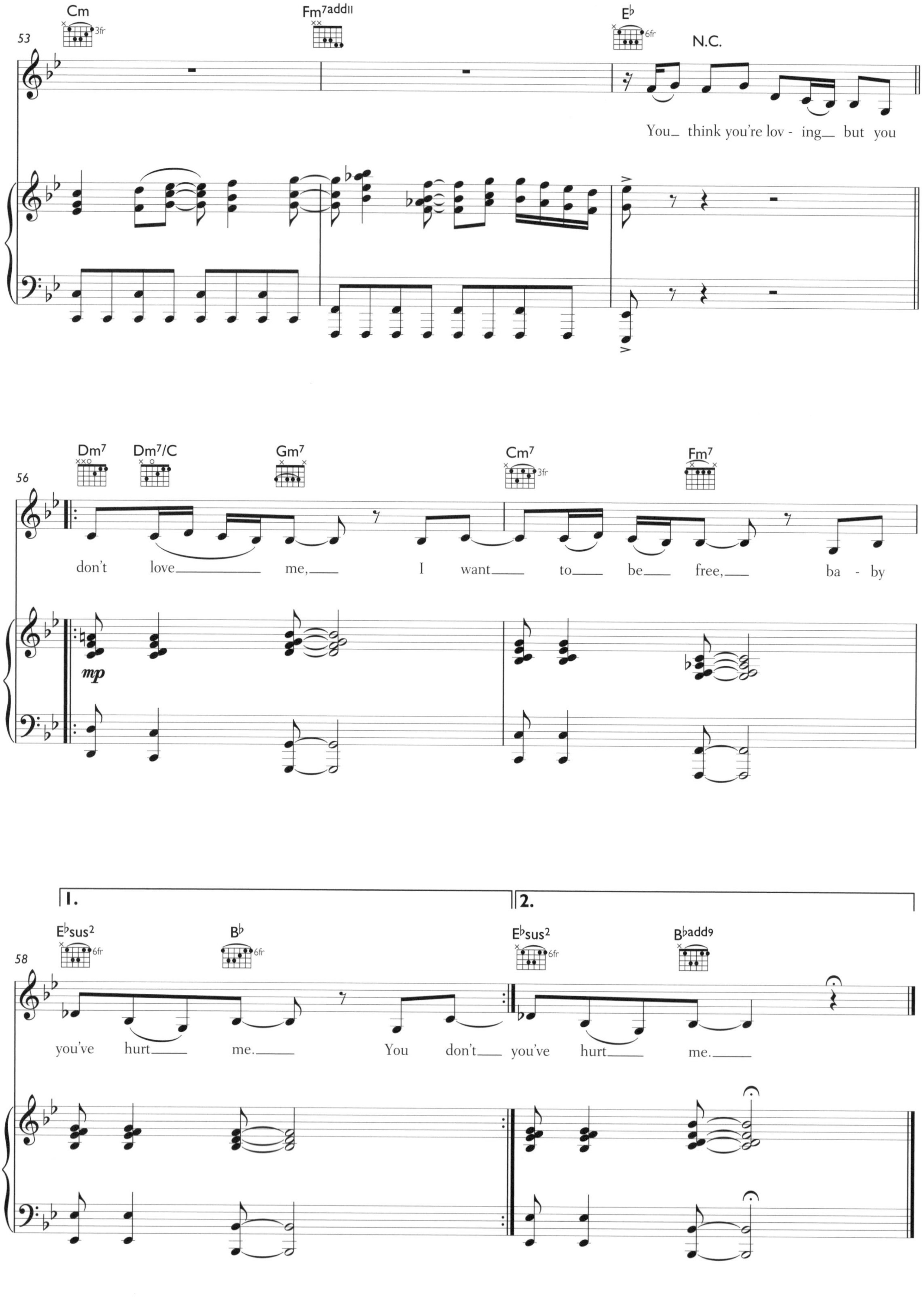
Cm
3fr
Fm7add11
E♭
6fr
N.C.
53
You_ think you're lov - ing_ but you
Dm7
Dm7/C
Gm7
Cm7
3fr
Fm7
56
don't love_ me,_ I want_ to_ be_ free,_ ba - by
mp
1.
2.
E♭sus2
6fr
B♭
6fr
E♭sus2
6fr
B♭add9
58
you've hurt_ me._ You don't_ you've hurt_ me._

WHAT ABOUT NOW

Words and Music by Ben Moody, David Hodges and Josh Hartzler

1.
2,3.
Em
D
D
8
and make it to the dawn.
To make it through the night,
I am by your side
(night,) love will find
(side) where love will find
F
C
Am7
11
you. What a - bout now? What a - bout to - day? What if you're ma-
f
Fadd9
C/E
Dm
C
C/B
14
- king me all that I was meant to be? What if our love ne-ver went a - way?

Am7
Am7/G
Fadd9
C/E
Dm
What if it's lost be - hind words we could ne - ver find? Ba - by, be - fore
C/E
To Coda
1.
F
Am
Em
it's too late, what a - bout now?
Mmm...
mf
2,3.
F
Dm
Am
(late,) what a - bout now?
Now that we're here, now that we've come
C
E7
Dm
this far, just hold on.
There is no - thing to fear,

Am Am/G G/F F G/F F F/E
30
for I am right be - - side you, for all
G/D Dm7 G/D Dm7 Am
33
my life I am yours.
C/G
36
What a - bout now? What a - bout to - day? What if you're ma -
mp
Fsus2 Dm7 Am
3fr
39
- king me all that I was meant to be? What if our love ne-ver went a - way?

C/G
Fsus2
3fr
Gsus4
G
D.S. al Coda
42
What if it's lost be-hind words we could ne - ver find. What a-bout now?
f
Coda
F
C/E
C/G
F
45
(late,) ba-by, be-fore it's too late, ba-by, be-fore
C/E
Fadd9
48
it's too late, what a-bout now?

James Blunt

YOU'RE BEAUTIFUL

Words and Music by James Blunt, Sacha Skarbek and Amanda Ghost

A♭(9)
E♭
13
Of that I'm sure. She smiled at me on the sub - way, she was
fly - ing high, and I don't think that I'll
B♭(11)/D
Cm7
15
with an - oth - er man. But I won't lose no sleep on that 'cause I've got a plan.
see her a - gain, but we shared a mo - ment that will last till the end.
A♭
B♭
B♭sus4
E♭
18
You're beau - ti - ful. You're beau - ti - ful. You're beau - ti - ful, it's true.
21
I saw your face, in a crowd - ed place,

Cm7 A♭ B♭ Cm7
and I don't know what to do, 'cause I'll nev-
1.
A♭ B♭ B♭sus4 E♭ B♭(11)/D
-er be with you.
Cm7 A♭(9)
2.
A♭ B♭ E♭
2. Yeah, she caught- -er be with you.
A♭(9) A♭6/9 A♭(9) A♭6/9 A♭(9) A♭6/9 F7sus4 B♭(11)/D
La, la, la, la. La, la, la, la. La, la, la, la la.

A♭ B♭ B♭sus4 E♭ A♭ B♭ B♭sus4
38
You're beau - ti - ful. You're beau - ti - ful. You're beau - ti - ful, it's true.
E♭ A♭ B♭ B♭sus4 E♭ B♭(11)/D Cm7
41
There must be an an - gel with a smile on her face, when she
A♭ B♭sus4 B♭ E♭ B♭(11)/D Cm
45
thought up that I should be with you.
A♭ B♭ Cm7 A♭(9) B♭(11)/D E♭
48
But it's time to face the truth, I will nev - er be with you.